MARY HAZARD
with Corinne Sweet

Sixty Years a Nurse

The heartwarming true story of one of the NHS's longest-serving nurses

HarperElement
An imprint of HarperCollins*Publishers*
1 London Bridge Street
London SE1 9GF

www.harpercollins.co.uk

First published by HarperElement 2015

3 5 7 9 10 8 6 4 2

A catalogue record of this book is
available from the British Library

ISBN 978-0-00-811837-2

Printed and bound in Great Britain by
Clays Ltd, St Ives plc

MIX
Paper from
responsible sources
FSC™ C007454

FSC™ is a non-profit international organisation established to promote
the responsible management of the world's forests. Products carrying the
FSC label are independently certified to assure consumers that they come
from forests that are managed to meet the social, economic and
ecological needs of present and future generations,
and other controlled sources.

Find out more about HarperCollins and the environment at
www.harpercollins.co.uk/green

To my wonderful family, and children Anthony and Christopher, and to Jennifer, whom I will never forget (MH)

To Corinne and Albert Haynes, for being there, and being you (CS)

Contents

Foreword

I first met Mary Hazard at my local GP's surgery, the Bounds Green Group Practice, when I moved into the area in 2000. She took my blood at the surgery one day, and I was immediately struck by her vibrant personality, her amazing manner and her fantastic sense of humour. It soon became very clear that Mary was an institution. Everyone at the surgery revered her, and when she took blood it was a painless experience, accompanied by laughter and goodwill. One day she told me a story about how the women come in and say to her, 'Will it hurt?' and she says, 'Yes, it's a little prick,' and they say, 'OK, go ahead,' and they're fine. And then the men come in, ask the same question, look brave and then, 'Boom, they're on the floor.' Mary is a larger than life, wonderfully warm, amazing character, always smartly dressed and up for anything (clubbing in a tiara in Leicester Square), and the surgery was not the same at all once she left in November 2013.

While writing this book I visited Mary one night at home and found a crowd of people round her front door, anxiously peering in her bay window. 'Where is she?' a worried neighbour said. 'Oh, she might be unconscious on the kitchen floor,' said another. Then some colleagues were visiting from the GP's surgery, and were worried: 'Where's Mary? We hope she's all right.' The friends and neighbours, colleagues and passers-by were so worried about losing Mary, they forced her front door open, only to hear her loud, commanding voice booming from the pavement: 'Sweet Jesus, what in hell do you think you're doing? Can't even go for a drink without being invaded?' This was then accompanied by a raucous laugh, and we all knew that Mary had been off on her own, doing her own thing, having a quiet drink with friends down the pub, her little dog in tow. Mary is a total people magnet, who belies her age. Her neighbours call her 'Queen Mary' as she knows all the business in the street, is everyone's friend, but always speaks her mind. Even at 80 she is never alone, since the doorbell goes constantly, as the phenomenon that is Mary Hazard attracts all comers.

This book only really scratches the surface of Mary's sojourn from Ireland to England in the early 1950s. The most amazing part of the story is that she is still here to tell the tale, and is still a force to be reckoned with, after

Foreword

62 years working in the NHS and 80 years of amazing, boisterous and, sometimes, tragic life.

Corinne Sweet

Acknowledgements

To Ivan Mulcahy, without whom this book would not have happened, and Sallyanne Sweeney, for your excellent assistance. To Natalie Jerome and Kate Latham, for brilliant feedback, editing and guidance. Thanks also for background research to Sgt Mark Bristow, of RAF Northolt. To my family, friends and NHS colleagues for being there for me down the years. To Rufus Potter and Clara Potter-Sweet for patience and forbearance as ever with the writing process.

1

Arriving from Ireland

It was so exciting: my first plane journey, *ever*. Also, my first proper time away from home, especially overseas. It was 10 September 1952, I was seventeen, and only a week away from my eighteenth birthday. I was so proud and independent to be sitting on this silver and dark-green Aer Lingus Bristol 170 Freighter, engines throbbing, propellers whirring, all the way from Dublin. I felt very grown-up, all on my own, with my little bag neatly stowed overhead and my new shiny black Clarks shoes on my feet. My heart was racing the whole time: I was finally on my way to fulfil a life-long ambition. As we descended through dank, grey clouds towards Northolt Airport, west of London, my stomach started churning and jumping in a wild fandango of fear and anticipation. What had I done? What would it really be like? What if my mother was right, and I wouldn't last a month? I slipped my hand into my skirt pocket, and there was the folded £20 note (about £400 today) for my return fare if I couldn't stand 'that evil, black Protestant Godforsaken country'. My mother had screamed, then sulked at me, right up until the last minute, when she had given me a reluctant, brisk kiss on the cheek goodbye. 'You'll need this for your return journey, you stupid, wayward girl.' She'd pushed a rosary, crucifix and little prayer book into my other hand, and stalked off, straightening her hat with its pheasant feather, with an irritated air. On the other hand, my father had folded me into his big arms saying, 'Let her go, Agnes, she has to find her way,' which made me sob into his firm, tweedy shoulder. 'Yer bladder's in yer bloody eyeballs,' he teased, as always, which made me laugh through my tears, cheering me up no end.

Now, as the plane descended noisily, bumping through the dense clouds, I noticed the airport buildings rushing up towards me. I leaned towards the window and held my breath: I could just make out dark-grey silhouettes of the Nissen huts, a huge black hangar and a lit-up runway through foggy, late-afternoon light. Suddenly, a front page of the *Irish Times* flashed across my mind of a fatal air crash only back in January, when the same kind of plane as mine had smashed dramatically into a Welsh mountainside. It was a very rare event, but the memory of twisted wreckage, fatalities and the image of a child's doll sinking into a bog made me shudder all the same. What on earth was I doing coming all alone to England? Maybe I *was* mad, like my mother said? Then I made myself get a grip: '*Come on, Mary, pull yourself together,*' I scolded myself. '*What are you thinking? It's all going to be fine. You'll see.*'

Once in the busy airport, I had to find my way to Putney, wherever on earth that was. It was a long, long way from Clonmel, in the south-west of Ireland, that's for sure. Everything looked so strange and grey, concretey and dull, after the lush green and spreading apple orchards of my beautiful home town. However, I made myself focus, as I wasn't going to be beaten at the first hurdle (I wouldn't give my mother that kind of satisfaction), and I soon managed to find a Greenline bus. A friendly conductor explained in broad Cockney I had to change twice to get to Putney: once in Ealing, and again in Richmond. His accent made me laugh, because it sounded so funny – the first English I'd ever really come across in person. All my life I'd dreamed of this moment, of going off to be a nurse. My mother had wanted me to study nursing in Dublin, under the beady, watchful eyes of relatives, but after a lifetime with the nuns, in convent school, I knew I could not bear another moment under their rigid, cruel control. This is where my mother and I came to bitter loggerheads, and the fight was set to continue, even though I was now in England, facing my first six months of State Registered Nurse (SRN) training. As I climbed aboard the coach, I realised it was going to be a long and memorable journey, in more ways than one.

Looking out the window, watching the unfamiliar English streets unfold, I realised I was finally escaping the confines of my home and upbringing to make this new, exciting but scary foreign start. It was 1952, and I was setting out on three years of intensive training. Ireland had been shielded, relatively, from the war, but as we drove towards London I could see bomb damage and that things were still quite austere in England. I was used to the green, lush land of Ireland, the river running past the end of our road, with its neat houses; England looked grey, suburban and a bit dreary. But it was all new to me, an adventure, and I'd finally escaped those religious, social and moral constraints that had driven me to become quite a rebellious girl.

Back home, I was the youngest of five children: four daughters, Una, Betty, Joan and me, Mary Francis, as well as a son, Peter Joseph – all of us with good Catholic names, of course. My mother, Agnes, was a seamstress and milliner, and had left school at fourteen to go into service at first. My father, George, had also left school early, but was bright, and had managed to get a good job in Customs and Excise, going around the bonded stores (which were like government-controlled warehouses), testing the specific gravity of all sorts of things, like rum and whiskey, so people didn't get short-changed or prosecuted for doctoring goods. We lived in a big, white-painted house opposite a weir on the River Suir, on the Raheen Road, five minutes outside of rural Clonmel. It was a lovely family house, with an apple orchard down the side of the house, and a huge rambling garden with wild roses and heather, high hedges and white metal gate. On one side of the house there were my mother's raised vegetable and fruit beds, and on the other there was a big lawn where my brother had created a little nine-hole putting course. We were quite well off, and my dad had a car (which few in the town had), a black, four-door Morris 10, which he would steer proudly up the drive, while being greeted noisily by our two liver and white Cocker Spaniels, Ivor and Vanda.

I'd wanted to be a nurse for as long as I could remember. I was always bandaging people, and pushing dolls and babies in my little black pram. I even helped a neighbour with Parkinson's, Mrs Roach, up the road. I didn't know what it was in those days, and there was no cure for it. This little old lady shook all the time and dribbled, and her daughter, Nora, gave up her life to look after her. I used to sit with Mrs Roach while Nora, who was a spinster in her fifties, went shopping, and I used to think, '*I wonder why she's like that? I wonder what can be done to help her, poor thing?'* I hadn't a clue, but I was fascinated, and I wasn't put off at all. I have to admit that I was a bit of a naughty child, a bit wild, I suppose. I liked climbing trees, and we nicked apples out of orchards. I loved wheeling real babies out in their high Silver Cross prams, too, and we used to wheel this baby, Frank, around, when he was about nine months old, and gradually fill up his pram with all these apples and pears we were stealing. One day, a man at the gate of an orchard stopped us, and when he pulled back the blanket, which was covering a huge lumpy heap, including a crying Frank, I was in big trouble. As my punishment, I got a walloping with a rolled-up newspaper from my father and was never allowed out with the big pram and baby Frank again.

We did go back in the orchards, though, for a different purpose. Magners and Bulmers were the local cider makers, they still are, and they had masses of huge apple orchards in Clonmel. We used to go round, in gangs of kids, with aluminium buckets and fill them up with windfalls. Then we'd get tuppence a bucket, and after a long day doing this we'd have two and six, or something like that. My father would match whatever I 'earned' and then I was told to put the money in my Post Office account. We did eat the apples sometimes, but they were so sour they made you wince. We rather preferred the hard cash instead – and this is the way my father taught me to save (for which I am very grateful). And it was fun – long days larking about in the sun, or rain, scrumping away, giggling and throwing rotten apples at each other.

Although there was rationing in Ireland, there was no bombing. In fact, the Irish usually sided with the Germans over the English, back then, because of our long history of strife. Because my father worked for Customs and Excise, he was well in with people, and got butter and other stuff on the black market, so we didn't go short. We were very lucky, where others weren't (which my mother was always reminding me of, of course). Plus, my mother was a great gardener and she would grow carrots, cauliflowers, potatoes, tomatoes, broccoli, cabbage, rhubarb, everything. I remember one day, when I was quite young, she had shouted at me about something, and, annoyed, I went out and pulled up all the baby carrots in one of her huge, beloved raised beds. I ruined the entire crop. My mother went ballistic and shouted the usual 'Wait till yer father gets home' threat. I tried to put the carrots back, but they were only like little fingers, and they were all floppy, and it was hopeless. I knew I was in for it, and I did get walloped – again with the rolled-up newspaper.

I think my parents loved each other, although they had quite a temperamental relationship. My mother was the 'boss', a 'matriarch', while father was the most gentle of gentlemen (at home, at least), apart from when he walloped me, which wasn't as often as my mother, who did it a whole lot more. Although she threatened us with father's 'tellings offs', she would meanwhile pick up the sweeping brush and make use of it by shaking it at us threateningly, or even hitting us, when pushed to the limits.

We all had to muck in and make the house nice, as she was very house proud, and she did everything herself. There were no 'mod cons', so the washing had to be scrubbed and wrung in the mangle on a Monday, the house cleaned and swept scrupulously, and the rag rugs, which my mother made by hand, had to be beaten on the line. I hated this job as the dust went in my mouth and eyes, up my nose, absolutely everywhere it possibly could. One day, when I was about ten, I was sitting on the stairs, grumpily, having to clean the brass stair rods, which held the stair carpet in place, one by one. I was supposed to pull each rod out, rub it with Brasso, put elbow grease into them until they shone, and then put them back in, at the base of the stair, through metal loops. The stairs were long and there were so many rods, so being me I tried to cut corners, but, of course, my mother caught me. Well, I was in for it. 'Mary Francis!' she shouted at me, and I tried to ignore her, until she was on me, pulling me off the stairs, and I was being hauled out for a walloping. I was supposed to go to the cinema that afternoon in Clonmel for sixpence, which I loved, and I was told there was no way would I be going out that day. I had to clean all the stair rods properly, all over again, through gritted teeth, until I could see my face in them. I knew I deserved it for being cheeky, but it still felt terribly unfair, so I blubbed the whole time I rubbed.

Another day, when I was about eleven, it was my turn to go and fetch the newly baked bread from the shop across the road. We had these large pan loaves and I loved the smell of freshly baked bread. Anyway, I couldn't resist, despite my mother warning me, 'If you eat that bread, I'll give you a bloody good hiding.' But the bread was not wrapped up, it was so lovely and fresh, so tempting and warm, and I tore off the end and gnawed it greedily on my way back home and up the garden path. When I got there, I knew I would be in trouble. My mother was very strong-willed, and she would hit me with whatever came to hand. Knowing this I popped the loaf in the porch and ran down the garden, out of harm's way. I thought, 'God, I'm going to get it now.' However, I then heard 'Mary, yer tea's ready,' and, being me, I thought it was all right and she'd not noticed. However, when I rushed in the front door I was immediately met by a blow to the head – with the loaf of bread. I tried to get away but she was shouting 'Mary, get in here, you evil little child,' and was hitting me hard. She got me in the eye. 'That'll teach you not to do this again,' she shouted. 'We've got to eat this bread.' So I ran outside, crying bitterly, and I found Ivor, our dog, and sat on the wall outside. He came and sat with me, so I lifted up his long furry ear, and blubbed into it, 'I hate her, I hate her,' very dramatically: my little heart was breaking. Then I saw my dad coming up the road. My saviour! Ivor would sense him coming and would go mad, wagging his tail and barking. So I was rubbing my eye all the time, pinching the skin and being vicious, making it all the colours of the rainbow. When he got out the car I went crying to him. He used to call me 'Moll', and he asked, 'What's the matter, little Moll?' and I replied pathetically, 'Look what she's done to me. She hit me with a loaf of bread, all for nothing.' I put on a good show, and he lifted me up and walked into the house. I remember his Anthony Eden hat (a Homburg), worn at a rakish tilt, which he tipped up with his thumb as he said to my mother, 'Agnes, can you not control your children? Do you have to maim them?' So with that she got a dishcloth and threw it at him.

Then she wouldn't talk to him at all, and we all seven of us sat round the big square scrubbed wooden kitchen table in total silence (sometimes one of us, in disgrace, would sit at mother's sewing machine to eat). Today, it was me in the doghouse, obviously. She wouldn't talk to me either, as I was the 'evil trouble-maker'. As she dished out she'd say things like, 'Betty, pass the salt to yer father,' or 'Will you ask yer father what he wants on his plate.' And then my father would say to Betty, 'Can you tell your mother the dinner was rotten.' I would also be sent to Coventry by my sisters, who blamed me for all the family trouble – so I would be in agony as well. All this would go on for at least a couple of weeks, until one of my big sisters would slap her cutlery down on the table and say in front of my parents, 'For God's sake, stop it, the pair of you!' And all the while I'd be sitting there, with my head down, feeling like I was all the cause of the trouble – which, of course, I was.

Then they'd make up and it would all be OK again. They had their traditions: once a year my parents would dress up and go to the policemen's ball or county farmers' ball together and have a grand old time. Father would also go out to the pub every night at nine o'clock sharp. McPhelan's, it was. My mother would get grumpy, but my father went, regular as clockwork, to meet his five handsome brothers, also known as the 'terrible five' locally, who would have pints and whiskeys, smoke smelly Passing Cloud cigarettes, and talk and plot politics late into the night. My mother would say to him, 'If I was dead in my bed, you'd still go to McPhelan's,' which was true, probably. Meanwhile, at home, she would be bottling fruit, making jam, doing sewing, knitting or crocheting, or giving us 'question time' round the table. She would be asking where Finland was on the map, or setting us tests. I learned more from her about geography and history than I did eventually at school. Mother was also great at playing cards and teaching us games. We all had to play a musical instrument (mine was the piano), and we'd put on little operettas, with all the costumes and everything, which my mother would run up beautifully.

My father also liked pheasant and grouse shooting, and he'd go out with his shotgun folded under his arm in his tweed jacket and big boots. He used to hang the smelly old dead birds up in the shed afterwards; I'd see all the blood running down into dark pools on the floor, and I'd hate it. My mother used to pluck them, and we used to eat them (there was loads of shot to pick out). One time he shot a cock pheasant and the feathers were absolutely beautiful. He had the bird stuffed and it would sit on top of the old piano that we all learned on, and my mother put the long tail feathers in her hats. However, my father hated having to go and ask for permission to shoot up at the big local estate, which used to be owned by the Duke of St Albans. 'It galls me to have to go cap in hand and get permission from those bastards. I don't see why I have to get permission from the bloody English to shoot on our own land.' There was a lot of animosity towards the

English in Clonmel, going back in history to a particularly terrible siege in 1650, with Cromwell massacring the locals willy-nilly. They found the bodies of mothers with babes in arms, and all sorts, in a mass grave, which caused a huge stir locally once the details were revealed in the 1950s. In his youth my father had been a fighter for Ireland's freedom, and he'd tell how the youths would get the Black and Tans and push them up against doors with their pitchforks and worse. I loved to hear these stories; they were thrilling and my father was a wonderful talker.

For instance, he told me that he was in the IRA as a young man, and he had a little silver gun, a revolver, which he kept down his sock. He said he was one of Michael Collins's men. He would tell wonderful stories, about men in Cork and the IRA, during the 1914–18 war and the twenties, which left me spellbound. He told me about escorting the Black and Tans out of prison. One day he was walking down a lane with my mother, hand in hand, when they were courting, and a 'Peeler' (an English policeman) jumped out of the bushes and confronted him on the road. My father said the Peeler made him strip down to his combinations (old-fashioned long-johns), and then he searched him, which was all done in front of my mother. It was hugely embarrassing for my mother, humiliating for my father, and then it all got ugly so she ran away in fear. When my father was bending down to undo his boot laces, he took out his little silver gun from his sock and shot the Peeler dead. The local men hid the body and it was an 'unsolved crime'. He was later decorated by the President of Ireland for shooting the policeman. When he died he was buried with full military honours, with the IRA flag draped over his coffin and shots fired over it. He was a hero in many people's eyes, including mine.

At the age of four I was sent to the Nuns of the Presentation Convent in Clonmel. They lived in a huge, gloomy greystone place, with a cloister in the middle in Irish Town, an outer part of Clonmel. I hated and detested it right from the very start until I finally left for England, at seventeen. All four of us sisters were sent to the Presentation Nuns, while my brother Peter Joseph, who everyone called P-J, went to the Christian Brothers. The nuns were cruel and vicious, and we were 'murdered' (by which I mean belted and walloped) regularly by them; and sadly P-J was equally cruelly treated at his school. Worst of all was Sister Margaret, who was tall, gaunt, with glasses, and who had a ghostly aura about her. She was particularly horrible, especially to me, or so it seemed. She was the Devil incarnate, and I used to come home crying to my mother after a bad day at school saying, 'I'm going to kill her,' and my mother would snap at me, 'You mustn't talk like that. You should try to be patient – why do you think she's a nun?' And I'd say, 'I don't know, but I guess her family hates her.' And my mother would 'tut' and then say, 'Nobody loves her, she has no family probably,' trying to make me feel sorry for her (which I didn't), as she always seemed to have it in for me, unfairly. We all knew that nuns were often farmers' daughters, who were shoved out into a convent when there were too many to marry off or feed and clothe – so they solved the problem by hastening them into the folds of the Church.

Anyway, I was always in trouble at school. I was a bit naughty, I admit; I remember there was a very goody-goody girl with a long plait, the end of which I stuck into an ink-well, and it went all black. I got into trouble for that, although I tried to play the innocent at the back of the class. Of course, I shouldn't have done it, but I think I was always in need of exerting myself against unfair authority. Sister Margaret would take us for knitting, sewing and the like, and one day she was teaching us moss stitch. I was sweating away, struggling to keep my stitches on my needle, while Sister Margaret prowled up and down the rows between the desks. She was in her long black uniform, with big sleeves, and a huge crucifix clunking round her waist, with her big starched hat, and a white starched bib down her front. On her hand she had a huge silver Bride of Christ ring. She hovered over me menacingly as I was struggling with the knitting, thinking, '*Sweet Jesus, I've lost a stitch. What am I going to do?*' 'Having trouble, are we?' snarled Sister Margaret, and she got her big ring and ground it hard against the side of my head. It hurt like hell. But if that didn't make me contrite enough, she'd take out her pencil, which had a sharp point, and would push it into my ear lobe as hard as she could. My eyes would spring with tears and I'd yelp. Then she'd drag everything off my needles in fury and throw it onto the desk, in front of everyone. Then I would be told to stand on my seat, and as we had glass partitions everyone in the adjoining classrooms would see me standing there, humiliated and blubbing. It was terrible. I would run home and tell my mother what had happened, but she'd just say I should 'pray for Sister Margaret's body and soul' and I would say, again, 'But, Mammy, I want to kill her, so I do.' I swear my ears were pierced before I was fourteen years of age.

Although my mother was quite tough, she was also very skilled and she could do anything with her hands. As she was a dressmaker, she was very nimble with her fingers, so at school I was wearing a black gym frock, with box pleats and a red sash, which had been let up and down endlessly as it had been worn by all my sisters before me. When I was about fourteen, the gymslip hem came just to my knees. Anyway, on this particular day Sister Angela, who was dumpy, with a big bust and wire glasses, was taking us for singing. She was a strict old thing, very punitive and cold, and I didn't warm to her. 'Stand out, Mary Francis,' she suddenly shouted at me, 'and look at the Virgin Mary – she's about to weep at your immodest legs.' I was jolted out of my musical reverie and looked at the statue on the wall and wondered what on earth I'd done now. Sister Angela came and stood over me and then made me get out in front of the class. I wanted to die. She then went and got a big sheet of brown paper and knelt down and stitched it to the hem of my frock, right down to the ankles. I felt so humiliated. My best friend, Jo Mulochny, who sat beside me, looked at me with big eyes and mouthed at me, 'Jesus, your mother'll go mad!' It was well known that my mother was proud of her family and skills.

At the end of the class Sister Angela snapped at me to stay behind, but I didn't – I ran out of the door like a bat out of hell, brown paper crackling as I went. It was pouring with rain, and I had to walk a mile home from school. So I was half walking, half running, with all this brown paper slapping round my legs, all wet and flapping. When I got in my mother was sat at the treadle sewing machine in the kitchen and I said, 'Look what she did to me.' My mother jumped up and said, 'Jesus wept, who did that?' 'Sister Angela,' I said, crying. 'She humiliated me over my gym frock. She said it was "immodest".' Well, that was it. My mother was enraged. She couldn't bear any of us being humiliated like that. She was a proud woman, especially about her dressmaking and mothering skills. She didn't care if we got belted, as she thought we probably deserved it, whatever happened, but this kind of deliberate public humiliation was the last straw for her. 'That's it!' she said. And it was – it was war. Her feather hat was on in a trice – she never went anywhere without her hat and her gloves – then she said 'Come on!' and we were out the door. My mother had a lame foot, but she was on fire, so we had to march right back to school, with it still raining, and my brown paper still slapping off my legs. She was going so fast that I was half-running, half-walking, as she was half-dragging, half-pulling me behind her. My mother was fuming, incendiary and about to explode.

When we got to the nuns' part of the school, to their living quarters, on a big, long corridor, we could hear them all singing piously at prayer. Butter wouldn't melt at all, so my mother rapped loudly on the door, and a little nun came limping out, the wizened housekeeper, Mother Anthony, leaning on her stick, all serene. In fact, she was the Reverend Mother, and she knew my mother well because my mother had gone to the school there, before me, also when she was little. I was tugging at my mother's coat, whispering, 'Mammy, let's go, she'll kill me tomorrow.' But my mother was adamant, and firmly planted to the floor: 'No, she won't. You leave this to me.' So when Mother Anthony said, 'Mrs Powell, how nice to see you. What can we do for you?' my mother exploded. 'Look what Sister Angela has done to my daughter. How dare she humiliate me and my family!' On and on it went, and I was so red, so embarrassed, I wanted to die.

Mother Anthony kept calm in the face of this and simply said she would deal with it, but my mother was not to be put off. 'You get that Sister Angela out here right now,' she insisted, eventually. Out Sister Angela came, looking sheepish and bland, and my mother let rip. 'Did you do this to my daughter's frock?' Sister Angela said not a word, but looked terrified. 'Get a pair of scissors and undo it now!' The paper was all dripping and flapping round my legs by now, creating a puddle on the floor. So Sister Angela removed the paper, obediently, but after that, and until the day I left, she totally ignored me. She made sure I was shoved down to the bottom of the class, however. But I was happy, because she left me alone.

I always liked people, and I was always interested in learning, although I often didn't pay attention to what my mother said, as I respected and feared her in equal measure – in fact, I usually did the opposite to what she wanted, quite cheerfully. When I was eleven we went on our usual summer caravan holiday in Tramore, which was an idyllic place by the sea, on the south-east coast of Ireland, just outside Waterford. This was probably the first time I ever learned about the evils of 'the Protestants in the North'. I made friends with a sweet girl there called Ann Jarvis and would go down and clamber over the rocks, then fish in the rock pools, and go swimming. It was lovely and I got on really well with this girl. Anyway, I was late back one evening and I brought Ann with me. My mother asked her where she was from and she said innocently, in her strange sing-song accent, which was different from mine, 'Belfast,' and 'We come down here every year.' My mother's face was like thunder as she pulled me into the caravan and pushed Ann out and slammed the door. 'Don't ever talk to her again,' she raged right in my face. 'She's a black Protestant from the North. We don't associ-ate with *those* people. They are not God-fearing people – they're all *hypocrites*.' And that was it. I was forbidden to talk to her ever again. It was really confusing as I'd thought she was a lovely girl, and I couldn't see her black soul, not at all.

Sometimes I'd get so fed up with my mother and her rules that I'd try to run away. When I was about fifteen I'd been in trouble again about something or other, and my mother had walloped me, so I decided that was it, I'd had enough, and I was off. It was dark, and we weren't allowed out at night, only to benediction, at the church. My mother was always suspicious of me, and rightly so, as usually instead of going to benediction (as I told my mother) I would meet up with a couple of girls from my class, fetch a purple Miners lipstick we had hidden in the hedge wrapped up in newspaper, and put it on, hitch up our skirts, and then go down to the quay to meet boys and smoke Woodbines. I had already started this filthy smoking habit very early, at about thirteen years of age, and I remember how they rasped your throat. It was like smoking a disgusting bonfire, but I felt I was very cool and 'grown-up', and we loved meeting up with the boys and feeling naughty. I'd rush back to the Friary at seven in the evening to see which priest was doing the 'Blessing of the Blessed Sacrament', then run home, wiping the purple off my lips with my sleeve, and wrapping the little lipstick back up in newspaper before popping it back in the hedge. When I got in my mother would say, 'Oh, you're back. Who said the blessing?' and I would rattle off the priest's name, sweet as you like. We sucked Polos to cover the tobacco smell. I don't think my mother guessed, although she always suspected.

Anyway, this miserable evening I was determined I was off for good. So I got some bread and wrapped it in a big handkerchief, as well as a snub of candle and two

Woodbines, before taking my father's big old bicycle, with the upright handlebar. I thought, *'Right, that's it. I'm never coming back. See if they miss me.'* My feet could hardly reach the pedals and it was only when I got to the other side of the town, and was near the cemetery, that I began to get the wind up, thinking, *'Oh my God, what am I doing? Oh, God, where shall I go?'* I suddenly felt very alone, very spooked and scared. Then I met my father coming out onto the road (he must have been looking for me), and he said, 'Ah, there you are. Where do you think you're going on that bike without a light?' I said, 'I'm running away ... but when I got to the cemetery, I got scared.' He looked at me and said, 'It's not the dead you fear, Mary, it's the living. Go home, and get that bloody bike in.' 'Yes, Daddy,' I said, secretly pleased he'd come to find me. So that was the end of my rebellious running away.

But now, today, in September 1952, at seventeen and all alone, I was finally on my three interminable bus journeys towards Putney in south-west London. I knew I wanted to be a nurse: I was utterly determined to succeed, whatever the odds. I could hear my mother's voice ringing in my ears, from all our endless fights, that England was 'taboo' and that 'no way was I to go to that Godforsaken

Protestant country'. But here I was, defying her again. My mother had a friend called Pat Wall, who lived in Wimbledon, and she wanted me to get in touch with her once I landed – 'She'll keep an eye on you.' Yes, I bet she would, as everyone always was keeping an eye on me, one way or the other. I said I would, but I knew I would try to avoid her like the plague, if I could. I didn't want any reports of my misbehaviour (if there was any, of course) to get back to my mother, as I knew she would be unbearable or, worse, drag me back, if I put a foot wrong.

Although I knew nothing about leaving home, nothing at all about travelling, or the world, for that matter, I knew I had to take this big step for myself. Eventually I found my way to Putney Hospital on that very long first day, and, as I rang the doorbell of the nurses' quarters, round the back of the enormous red-brick hospital on the edge of a huge common, I held my breath until the large wooden door opened. A small woman appeared, in a crisp navy uniform and stiff white cap – she gave me a quick once-over while I explained who I was. After a pause she said, 'I'm Sister Matthews, your Home Sister,' in clipped English tones. 'Come on in, you've had a long journey. I'll show you to your quarters.' And without a moment's hesitation, in I jolly well went.

2

Joining the Regiment

When I arrived in 1952, Putney Hospital was a rather handsome, red-brick Edwardian sprawl on leafy Putney Common in south-west London. The three-storey nurses' home was at the back, on the north side, and when I got there part of it had only just finished being rebuilt after being firebombed during the war in 1944 (it was the first incendiary bomb to land on London, in fact). I also found out, soon after, that there was supposed to be a ghost of a man dressed in a convict's uniform (including broad black arrows), who had apparently drowned in a pond, and now glided across the common on dark nights, seemingly intent on committing a crime. The story was he had been in Putney Hospital and now local people spoke of his haunting the place from time to time. But even further back it seems the hospital was built on old plague burial grounds, where people who died of the 'Pest' in 1625 were taken out of London and buried, so the link between

Putney Common, illness and death seemed to have a long, tragic and mysterious history. The place was green and spacious, but could also feel a bit eerie at night.

Anyway, by day there were nurses and sisters scurrying everywhere, being briskly busy in their starched, neat uniforms. It did strike me as ironic, momentarily, that I'd finally escaped the overly strict and pious regimes of home and convent in Ireland, only to end up with women wearing very similar outfits, albeit overseas and in a different context. However, I told myself, sternly, if I wobbled in my resolve, that I had battled to get here, and this was my own new adventure, so I was going to make it work, *whatever* I had to do – or *wear*. And no matter what anyone was like (they surely couldn't be worse than Sister Margaret). A recent memory of fighting with my mother was still ringing in my ears, with her screaming, 'You're not going!' and me shouting back, 'Yes, I am, I am, I AM going to England. You can't stop me!' (accompanied by another walloping and loads of tears). We were like two cats in a bag, with my sisters and father needing to intervene before we drew blood.

My first few days in Putney went by in a blur: it was all a bit like going to boarding school (or so I imagined). First, I had to be fitted out for my uniform. On the ground floor of the nurses' home, at the back of the main hospital, away from the road, there was a sewing room, with three middle-aged women stuck in it all day, sewing away happily at their Singer treadle machines. Lily, Gladys and Grace had to measure me up. They also worked out what each nurse needed individually, and then made it on the spot. It was a real home from home, for me, as I could imagine my mother being there, too, tape-measure round her neck, pins in her mouth, peering critically at their handiwork and 'tutting' at their sloppy stitches (*'Will you take a look at that – really!'*). The women's job was to actually make our uniforms, and then adjust them or re-use them, passing them on from nurse to nurse (definitely familiar 'make-do-and-mend' territory for me, especially reminiscent of the lean war years).

I was to be issued with three uniforms, so I would have one on, and one off in the hospital laundry, which was also on site, and one spare (as they always got dirty somehow). The dresses were pale-blue and white fine pinstriped, thick cotton, and down to our ankles nearly. We were also issued with seven white, starched aprons, one of which had to be pinned at the bib, at the front, and tied round the waist (I'm proud to say that mine was a tiny sixteen inches then). There were also starched collars and cuffs, which we had to keep absolutely spotless. Both aprons and cuffs had to be changed immediately they got mucky, which they obviously did on the ward, as we didn't have plastic aprons or rubber gloves back then. Also, if we rolled up our sleeves to the elbows, we had to put on elasticated white cuffs to keep them up and smart.

Underneath the uniform we were to wear thick black Lyle stockings, which had to be darned immediately if you got a run or snag (we did the darning at night, ourselves). This was all finished off by black lace-up sensible shoes, which had to be buffed until they shone. There was an absolutely 'no jewellery' rule, except for a brooch-style Smiths watch that I pinned on my right apron breast. This was to be used for taking patients' pulses. Also, definitely no make-up allowed, and our nails had to be inspected daily for cleanliness. Then hair had to be scrimped back tightly under our hats and any wayward hair (and mine was extremely wayward, like the rest of me) had to be pinned tightly into place. In fact, I'd cut off my beloved black plait, which reached nearly to my waist, in Ireland before I came, to my mother's horror, so I had a newly manageable short style with a fringed bob.

Most importantly, our belts reflected our status: a virginal white belt for our first year, a royal blue one for our second and a serious black one for our third. This last belt had a special silver buckle which denoted we'd made it through, once we'd passed all our exams and had qualified – and survived. But what I really loved, most of all, were the outdoor capes. We had waist-length navy-blue woollen capes with a fabulous crimson lining, which we wore over our uniforms. It was a real Florence Nightingale touch and I felt wonderful in mine. They had red cross-over tapes to keep them in place – oh, I did feel like a proper nurse as I flounced along, my cape swishing in the wind. Very heroic, like something out of a film like *Gone with the Wind*.

But, horror of horrors, there were the hats. At first, making my hat correctly (which I had to most days) seemed like trying to climb a mountain like Everest (which wouldn't be conquered until the next year, in 1953). We were given a fiercely starched square of white linen and we were taught by Sister Tutor (our lovely teacher, Angela Frobisher, who was kind, motherly and stocky), over and over, how to fold it into proper nurse's attire. It seemed a total impossibility at first and I was all fingers and thumbs. I was half waiting for Sister Margaret's ring to grind itself into my fumbling fingers or thump me in the temple, as I struggled to fold the blasted thing into a butterfly shape resembling a pukka Putney nurse's hat. I had to fold it on my knee, and then pleat it, and it had to be pinned to my head, perfectly. The air would turn blue while I struggled, at first. In the third year, when we became staff nurses, we got two strings and a bow under our chins, as did the sisters, so the hats looked like little bonnets. The hats also changed in shape according to status: so staff nurses' hats were different from Sister's, which was different from Matron's, whose was the most elegant and refined. We did look a sight, but I was secretly pleased and proud at finally being eligible to wear a trainee nurse's hat at all.

The nurse' home was at the north end of the hospital, and was three storeys high. We first years were on the middle level, with the second and third years on the top floor, and the doctors' on call and sisters' night duty sleeping rooms (separate, of course) on the ground floor. Our own bedrooms were small, cell-like but pleasant; clean, but very basic. I could see a large rambling lawn out of my window and, beyond it, Putney Common's trees and bushes and local red-brick terraces. There was a single bed, with a wooden headboard, a tiny gas fire (no central heating then), an ottoman (storage chest), wardrobe, a little basin under the window and a small brown dressing table and mirror. I had two pairs of flowery winceyette pyjamas and a vest, which my mother insisted on me wearing to keep warm.

I had to learn a whole new routine. A maid knocked on the door at six thirty every morning, and I had to get straight up, spit spot, no messing. In the winter, it was tough to get up to no heating and in the dark. I had a quick wash at the basin, then it was on with all the uniform, and a clean apron (which crossed over at the back) every day. There were no tights then, so the Lyle stockings were held up with suspenders which hung from a suspender belt, which we wore over our knickers. When we lost our suspenders, we used buttons or pennies which we twisted in the tops to keep our stockings up. We were allowed silk as we got more senior, and tights (American Tan, of course) didn't come in until the early 1960s – so thick, mendable stockings were the rule. In my pockets I always had to have a pen and a pair of scissors – and my only allowed adornment was my little pinned-on watch. When our clothes were dirty we put them outside the door, in a marked laundry box, and they were taken away and laundered and brought back crisply starched and ironed in a week. It all had to be absolutely perfect.

Then I had to make my bed, using 'hospital corners' at the ends with the sheets and blanket, folded over tightly like an envelope shape, to keep everything in. Then I had to tidy my room for daily 'inspection'. There was no privacy at all, as Home Sister would suddenly burst in, unannounced, and if your room was not tidy, or the bed corners not made properly, she would rip off all the bedding and throw it on the floor and shout, 'Do it again, nurse, not good enough!' Or she would throw open my dressing-table drawers and, if things were not tickety-boo, tip the contents out onto the floor, and snap, 'No, no, no, this will never do – now tidy it up, nurse. Jump to it.' I was actually quite tidy by nature – my mother had trained me well – so I was pleased when Home Sister pronounced after a couple of weeks, 'Tidiest drawers in the whole place, Powell. Well done.' It was like one of those *Carry On* films, very Hattie Jacques. It was hilarious. After so many years with the nuns I felt there was nothing I couldn't handle, although Home Sister was very scary at first.

On Sunday mornings we went to church. So it was up at seven, and then we would be trooping down the road together to mass. We had to put money in the collection, but because we were broke most of the time we'd put in our stocking buttons or anything else that came to hand, much to the Father's disdain. Then we had to be in bed by ten o'clock at night and there was official 'lights out'. It was a complete institution and there was no messing about it. It was certainly like my home all over again. In fact, the nurses' home was like I imagined a strict boarding school would be like in the kind of Angela Brazil book that I had loved reading back home. I'd run away from the overly pious and unforgiving strictness of Ireland only to land in another fierce regime.

We earned ten pounds a month while we were training. Right from the beginning we needed to buy Woodbines from Bert the porter. I had learned to smoke surreptitiously at thirteen, and, sad to say, smoking had already become an essential part of my life, ironically for someone concerned about health. Of course, we didn't make the connection between smoking and health back then, as doctors often recommended cigarettes to patients to relax them. It was seen as a sophisticated pastime and almost everybody did it, without thinking. Plus, I was always hungry and tired, so smoking was a way of quelling my appetite and exhaustion. Buying the Woodbines, which were fiercely strong, was a total secret, of course, but we knew when we got our wages the first person we paid was Bert – and at four old pennies for a packet of eight, it soon mounted up. Bert would keep a tab when we didn't have any money, and we'd have to cough up (literally) once our wages came in. He would also get us the Merrydown cider that we liked to drink illicitly after lights out, to relax and have a giggle, so we could easily spend a third of our wages without even going out of the nurses' home. Our daily food was served in the hospital dining room. It was cooked on site, and was very basic. It was always quite plentiful and hearty, but stodgy: pies, puddings, potatoes, lots of starch. I remember we were always starving, and always demolished what was on our plates.

In 1952, Putney took in about twenty new trainee nurses – mostly from Ireland, like me, but also from

Holland, Germany, Hungary, Italy and England. There were strong unresolved post-war feelings and I'm sorry to say that racism abounded, unchecked. Matron, a small, intense woman called Miriam Sturgeon, said quite baldly to us that 'I'll take the Irish, because I need you, but I don't have to take the coloureds.' However, the Dutch would not sit down with the Germans, even if they were Jewish, and there was a hell of a lot of strife between them then, which I found quite bewildering at first. One of my first new trainee friends was a lovely Dutch girl called Hanse. She was nineteen and from Amsterdam, and she told me the most terrible story which explained her attitude towards the Germans. She said her family had been starving during the German occupation, and had had to beg, borrow or steal anything to eat. She had a twenty-year-old brother who would go out and forage for food, scavenging round the fields around Amsterdam or even dustbins. To disguise himself, he would put on one of Hanse's dresses and a headscarf, and get on her sit-up-and-beg bike, and go and scrounge turnips from the fields for the family to eat.

Then one day he was actually stopped by a German soldier. The Nazi asked what 'she' was doing, then tried to rape Hanse's brother, but when he discovered very quickly that 'she' was a boy, he shot him and left him in the gutter to die. As a consequence, Hanse would not sit down with the German nurses in the canteen, and hated being anywhere near them. She would stand up and eat, her back to the wall, and Sister would command, 'Sit down, nurse,' and Hanse would retort, saying, 'No, Sister, I'm fine where I am.' I'd be thinking, '*Oh, sweet Jesus, she's in for it*,' and I'd entreat her to sit down next to me. 'I'm not sitting next to a *verdammte Deutsche*,' she'd spit. I didn't really understand the depth of her feelings or the reasons for them then at all. I was so naïve back then. But Hanse would say, 'You know, Mary, the Germans killed us in Holland, just because we were hungry, so I'm not sitting down.' Another Dutch girl, Christe Lemm, would say, 'I'm also not sitting down next to those Germans. You can't make me,' and would stand staunchly next to Hanse. Infuriated by this insubordination, Sister would stride off and get Matron, telling her there was a war still going on with the prelim nurses; Matron would then march back in, alongside Sister, and snap at the Dutch protesters, 'Have you no dignity, girls? Sit down.' Unperturbed, Hanse would say, 'G*ott verdammt* the lot of us.' Matron would bark, 'Well, you'll all have to learn to rub along together. The war is over now.' Indeed, on the wards she would not settle for anything else, despite Hanse's and Christe's painful feelings. We were told over and over we all had a job to do, and we had to get on and do it, regardless of any personal grudges or feelings. But the Dutch and the Germans were red rags to a bull, while the Irish were stuck in the middle with the English, for a change. For me, this was a real turn-up for the books.

My training as an SRN would take three years, with each year including three months of day duty, three months of night duty, and experience on specialist wards, such as tuberculosis (TB), which was rife at the time. I was also to do a three-month stint in theatre and I would have to do dreaded annual exams. For the first three months I was at school daily being trained, and then I 'observed' on the wards for a day a week. We were only unleashed on the wards, to do some basic or minor tasks with real patients, under the eagle-eyed gazes of staff nurses and sisters, after the first three months were completed satisfactorily.

Even then, once on the wards, a lot of my time was spent cleaning: swabbing, washing, scrubbing, wiping everything down scrupulously. There was an unrelenting fixation on cleanliness and disease prevention, so we disinfected and scrubbed everything in sight. It was second nature. One of my first jobs was cleaning a toilet, without a brush or rubber gloves, which was disgusting. I was crying all the time, and Sister snapped at me to 'Stop blubbering and get on with it.' I said, 'My mother wouldn't make me do this,' and she said, 'Well, tough, nurse. You're not with your mother now, are you?' My hands became raw from washing and scrubbing all the time, immersed in carbolic and disinfectant, but there was a zero tolerance to infection as little could be done, otherwise, to stop it spreading. We didn't suffer from MRSA or C. Diff, which are the modern killers, but I'm convinced it's because we were on our knees wiping down the beds, even the chair feet and bed wheels, cleaning taps, washing down walls, even light switches, door knobs and bed springs, night and day.

Men and women were segregated into separate wards back then, and there were two main categories: medical (which was general and covered lots of things) and surgical. Each long, rectangular ward had up to thirty patients each, in beds down the sides, with the nurse's table at the double door end. There was usually a table for mobile patients to eat at down the middle of the room. The floors were wooden, and scrubbed constantly. There was a little side kitchen, where the nurses could make tea and toast, or squash, or fill vases and jugs with water. Also, there were balconies with iron railings outside the windows, and 'isolation' patients would be pushed out there in their beds to get fresh air (in which there was a great curative belief) during the day. There were a few side rooms for extremely ill or even private paying patients. Then, off the ward, there was the huge sluice, a big tiled room with huge sinks, for the metal bedpans and men's glass wee bottles to be washed and disinfected in. We also did diabetic urine testing there.

The women's medical ward, Corry, had patients in together with all sorts of different conditions from broken femurs with patients strung up on huge metal traction frames, to appendectomies, tonsillectomies (which were popular then), stomach ulcers and even women being treated for failed abortions. I was really amazed to see these poor women, of all ages, both married and single (which was shocking then), in with everyone else. Sister would 'tut tut' all the time, showing she did not approve of them, and they could be ostracised. Some of them came in in a terrible state, it was so cruel to see, with metal back-street abortion implements still stuck in them. But they got no kind words from Sister, no arm round the shoulder: she disapproved and she didn't mind showing it. They'd be given Ergometrine, a drug to put them in labour, and they suffered dreadfully, poor things.

Then we would be told to swab the women down with Dettol, and we'd have to shave them 'down there'. I'd never seen anything like this at all. The poor, bleak women would be rolled away to have a 'scrape' in theatre and then shoved back out by a very snooty Sister, as soon as she could discharge them. Then their 'incomplete abortions' would be lined up in metal bowls in the sluice for doctor to inspect. I was horrified. I'd see something baby-shaped, lying amid large liver-like clots of blood. She made the poor women feel very guilty about wasting her time and effort, and the Health Service money. It was a very bad business, a real eye-opener, and it made me feel very wary about getting pregnant, I can tell you.

The men's surgical ward, Lancaster, could be equally as grim. Among the broken legs and car smashes were the hernias, appendectomies and the constipated men ('who couldn't go'). The men's Lancaster Medical Ward was next door, and they had those 'incurable patients' with 'growths' (what we would now call cancer). It seemed so undignified and unnecessary to me for simple cases to be next to fatal ones. Then, if a man had to be shaved 'down there', I learned to beg Percy the porter to come and do it with a wet razor. Imagine my horror at being asked to exfoliate (yes, standard practice in disease prevention or pre-operative) a man's privates, when, as an innocent seventeen-year-old, I'd never seen a boy naked at all. But there were times, during those first months, when I had to do it all alone, and I was a quivering wreck, hoping and praying to God that my hand wouldn't slip at the wrong moment, and in the wrong place (I could hear Sister Margaret shouting at me that I was a 'clumsy oaf and a silly girl', which made it all so much worse).

So for the first three months in training school, being taught by Sister Tutor, I sat and took copious notes and absorbed as much knowledge as I could. It was all anatomy, physiology, hygiene and everything else thrown in. We had a large school room with a pink rubber woman dummy called Araminta that we had to practise all sorts of unspeakable things on. The walls were lined with shelves with things like a twenty-foot tapeworm suspended in formaldehyde, or miscarried babies in bottles. It could be a bit gruesome. But I soon got used to it, as I soon got used to everything else about hospital life. I can honestly say these months were spent swimming in blood, poo, vomit, wee and absolutely everything else that comes out of the body: it was a real baptism of bodily fluids.

3

Settling In

There was so much to learn in those first weeks and months that I was in a constant whirl of activity, confusion and, often, amusement and bemusement with my fellow trainees. We worked six-day weeks and there was a huge amount to learn, a great deal to absorb, mentally, and also to master, physically. For some reason, I was often clumsy, and I was also very naïve, although always very enthusiastic. So, I would find myself being barked at by the Day Sister Burton ('No, Powell, you don't do it that way, silly girl!') or Staff Nurse ('For goodness' sake, Powell, you're not wrapping a Christmas present – retie your bandage properly, now!') It was like being with my mother or Sister Margaret all over again – I could never get things right, or so it seemed.

We had to observe the doctors' rounds on the wards each week and I was absolutely fascinated by everything. We trailed behind the doctors and consultants in their crisp white coats and pin-striped suits, stethoscopes slung round their necks, as they pronounced on the patients and snapped their orders with military precision. We were like well-behaved little goslings following behind giant ganders. Staff and Sister would always be turned out perfectly, in smart navy uniforms, and would be beside the doctors, silently obedient, and at the ready, with notes and charts at hand, ready to answer their queries or to jump to it, as they talked loftily over the patients' heads. It was all very formal, intimidating – and bewildering. We nurses had to make sure everything was tickety-boo before the doctors did their rounds: everything had to be spotless, tidy and gleaming; sheets neatly tucked in, patients washed and hair combed. Their lockers had to be clean, with fresh water in their jugs and their flower vases refreshed. Sometimes I thought we made the beds so tightly that I wouldn't have been surprised if we had cut off the circulation in the legs and arms of the poor people strapped neatly into bed, like strangulated sausages in hot-dog buns.

Back in our training school on the ground floor of the hospital (safely away from the real patients) we had our large rubber dolly, Araminta, to practise clinical procedures on. She lay, smiling her unchanging red-lipped smile, on a bed, and she could be zipped open from chin to pubic bone, so we could take all of her plastic internal organs out: liver, spleen, stomach, intestines, gall bladder, kidneys, bladder, and so on. We spent quite some time taking Araminta apart and putting her back together again: it was quite a game. We also had to pretend to 'bed bath' Araminta, and change her rubber undersheet, which involved rolling her onto her side, sliding the 'drawsheets' out from under, and rolling her back again. She sometimes rolled onto the floor, which, obviously, we knew we'd have to avoid with real patients (if at all possible). However, Araminta didn't object to her mistreatment and sometimes we felt quite sorry for the punishment we gave her as we also had to practise giving her injections, which I hated doing. Back then syringes were made of glass and metal, and had to be re-used, so they were boiled in big metal sterilisers, which were bubbling away in the corner of the medical rooms all the time. Everything had to be boiled and sterilised endlessly, and was rejected as sub-standard if it wasn't perfectly clean.

Then one day, towards the end of my first three months, Sister Burton told me I was going onto the men's surgical ward and I was going to give my first injection. I nearly fainted. A *real injection into a real person. Not Araminta? No, surely not. I wasn't ready, was I?* Sister being Sister was blunt, business-like and to the point: 'Nurse Powell, you will give the patient his injection – now stop fussing and get on with it. You know what to do.' So I approached Mr

Brown's bed gingerly. I stood, holding the metal kidney-shaped dish with the syringe rattling in it, while he read his newspaper, totally unaware of my inexperience. He was a good-looking, fair-haired man of about thirty with a deep, badly infected cut on his leg from a work accident. He was sitting there, all innocence, in his striped pyjamas with no idea what was about to be unleashed on him – *all-fingers-and-thumbs-me*.

Mr Brown looked up and saw me looking at him fixedly, just as I felt a presence begin hovering behind me. I looked round and there was Sister, glaring. Oh my God, I had to get on with it. I pulled the screens round the bed on their squeaky wheels while I was frantically trying to remember what I'd done to poor old Araminta. Sister had told me the injection, which was a thick antibiotic mixture, had to go in the outer quadrant of Mr Brown's right buttock. Buttock! Sweet Jesus, I'd never seen a man naked before and now I was going to be looking at this poor man's bum, and inject him, to boot. Despite my nervousness, I tried to brazen it out: 'All right, Mr Brown, I have to give you this little injection, so could you roll over and pull down your pyjama bottoms?'

I couldn't believe I was saying this to a real, live man, and was even more amazed when he rolled over obediently, and did just that. Luckily, he couldn't see my hand shaking as I got the large syringe out of the dish and prepared it for him. Little it was not. I swabbed his right buttock with antiseptic and cotton wool, trying not to take in the smooth brown and hairy skin of his muscular body. I was looking at a naked man's posterior, my first, but was seriously trying to concentrate on the job in hand (as it were). I filled the syringe with the thick Streptomycin with trembling fingers, and pushed out the air bubble, just as I'd been taught. Surely nothing could really go wrong?

Thing was, I was terrified of hurting him and I stood rooted to the spot for a minute trying to remember all that Sister Tutor had told me when I was torturing Araminta. Mr Brown was perturbed by my hesitation. 'Anything wrong, nurse?' he asked, innocently, trying to peer round over his shoulder. 'No, no, nothing, Mr Brown,' I stuttered. 'No, not at all – just turn round, lie there and relax.' And with that I lobbed the heavy glass syringe at poor Mr Brown's right buttock, rather like a dart at a dart board, and it went in a bit, and then hung out of his bum at a ghastly angle. I knew it wasn't in right, especially as he yelped, then hollered, loudly, and to cover my embarrassment I just syringed the viscous fluid in as fast as I could. It should have gone deep in his muscle; instead I injected it all under his skin. Poor Mr Brown was groaning as I could see a ball forming under his epidermis, like a ping-pong ball. *Oh sweet Jesus!* I tried to make it better by rubbing his buttock a great deal, and sort of massaging it;

then I asked him to turn over and hoped for the best. The poor man looked pained, as he pulled his pyjamas up, but I tried to cheer him up as I tucked him in tightly before getting away as fast as I could.

Next day, I was really for it. Poor Mr Brown had now developed a deeply infected buttock. I was taken back to him, by Sister, and made to look: his buttock had gone black, and the place I'd injected had formed an ulcer. There was now a large hole which had to be packed. Mr Brown got really ill after this. My terrible injection technique was causing him almost more trouble than the leg injury that he had come in for in the first place. I felt absolutely awful, and was in floods of tears. *Sweet Jesus, I was hopeless, I would never make it – my mother was right, I was utterly useless.* I apologised profusely to Mr Brown, and to my utter amazement he was quite accepting about it. 'Never mind,' he said. 'It could have been worse.' He could see I was genuinely distraught. Worse? I didn't think it could be, and I seriously considered if I was really up to the job for the first time since arriving.

I was carpeted by Sister, who was a real dragon. 'What on earth do you think you were doing, Nurse Powell?' She went on and on, saying, 'We obviously can't let you anywhere near injections yet,' as I blubbered in front of her, wanting the floor to open up. I explained that I hadn't wanted to hurt poor Mr Brown, and instead I'd ended up giving him a whole load of pain. She barked at me to practise again on Araminta and stop whining. It was so humiliating as everyone on the ward knew it was me who had buggered it up and I imagined all the patients refusing to let me touch them from now on. *Her? Oh, no, I don't want her, Sister. Bring me a proper nurse. She's the Devil incarnate*. I could just hear it. Wisely, Sister moved me onto another ward the next day, telling me to 'Toughen up, Powell.' I certainly never gave another botched injection like that again; I learned I had to be firm and decisive from the start. Mr Brown recovered completely, I'm glad to say, and bore me no grudge. Luckily, patients didn't sue in those days or I'd certainly have been up for the chop.

There was another time I showed myself up badly, too. We had to go to the morgue, which was also on the ground floor at the back of the hospital, and observe a post-mortem as part of our training. I was very nervous about this as I had not seen a dead body as yet, although Araminta had been taken apart and put back together like a giant female plastic Meccano set several times over. I was very intimate with her by now – but a real dead body? This brought back horrors of Clonmel cemetery and the terror I always felt there after dark with my wild imagination seeing grisly ghouls and hellfire and damnation everywhere. I was never very good with horror films, ghosts or anything spooky like that. Even the thought of the Putney Common convict ghost made me shiver, and I tried to put it out of my mind as much as I could.

So one cool winter afternoon eight of us trotted along to the morgue, feeling we were going to the gallows. We were all extremely nervous at what might be about to happen, and getting each other nervous, plus my overactive imagination was working away, as usual. I didn't really know what I was in for until the mortician, a Mr Tayler, a lofty, serious-faced consultant, pulled back the shroud and there was a stark naked middle-aged man, the colour of putty: stone cold dead. I could feel my knees going immediately, so I crossed my arms and wrapped my fingers tight round my elbows to try to keep myself from falling over. There were lots of shiny, ordinary-looking surgical implements laid out, like a chisel, a carving knife, and then I espied something like a garden saw. Surely he wasn't going to use those? I closed my eyes and swallowed.

When I opened them again, the mortician picked the saw up cheerfully and without further ado deftly hacked through the top of the man's head. I stood there open-mouthed, and was amazed to see his brain fluid, like a grey, wrinkled, deflated football, which he scooped neatly in a silver bowl, explaining all the while about the nature of brain matter. Four of the assembled nurses went down immediately, like skittles, and one ran out, holding her hand over her mouth. Completely unperturbed, Mr Tayler continued his butchery, talking coolly all the while. I couldn't really concentrate and could feel my gorge rising, but I was determined to see it through, so dug my fingers into my arms even harder. Then Mr Tayler got his scalpel and cut the poor man's body from the neck to his pubes and suddenly all his guts were tumbling out, like miles and miles of grey sausages into a great silver tray alongside the slab … that was it, I was done for: I felt my knees buckle as the room spun round and I was sick as a dog on the floor.

When I came round I was outside on a chair, along with five other white-faced nurses, most of whom were bent double, holding their heads in their hands, and groaning. We were all told, in no uncertain terms, by a tough staff nurse, that we had to pull ourselves together straight away and get back in there. We were wasting valuable time, and this was part of our training – we were here to learn and we'd better get used to it. So after a few more woozy minutes and a sip of water we all had to troop back in and carry on watching as Mr Tayler cheerfully continued his controlled carnage, whether we liked it or not.

* * *

After a tough experience like my first injection, or the nauseating post-mortems, we took refuge in each other's rooms at night to put the world to rights and, literally, let our hair down. I had begun to make some firm friends in those first few months: Rosie, Hanse, Magdelena, Christe and Susan, who would keep me sane over the next three years one way or another. We would all club together and nip out to the local pub and get us a couple of bottles of Merrydown cider, our favourite tipple, and a couple of packs of Woodbines (often from Bert the porter). This was standard fare for a good nattery debrief. We'd pile into my room (nearly always mine for some reason), and we'd be on my bed, cackling, gassing, recounting the horrors of the day until lights out, and beyond.

One night I drank a bit too much (as was my wont), and I was desperate for a pee. We had the windows open to waft the smoke out (smoking was totally forbidden, of course), and I realised I was too far gone to get up and find the lavatories at the end of the corridor. Being clumsy, I would probably alert Home Sister Matthews by staggering about, and then we'd all be for it. So, we closed the windows, giggling, and I decided I would pee in the sink to save time. This increased the suppressed laughter ten-fold, especially as I tried to hitch up my skirt and bum onto the tiny hand-basin and position myself to pee properly without flooding the floor. 'Oh, Mary, be careful,' Susan was just saying when there was an almighty 'craa-aack' and the sink came away from the wall, tipping me onto the floor, with my pants round my knees in a pool of water. The four witnesses fell off the bed in complete hysterics, and we all lay helplessly on the wooden floor for about five minutes until we heard Home Sister's footsteps begin to clip down the corridor. 'Sssshhhh,' I said, and everyone mimicked, 'Sssshhhh!' and we all lay there, panting and trying to suppress our mounting hysteria, waiting for Sister to barge in with a torch. Luckily, we heard her feet pause, then begin to retreat, thankfully, once we managed to shut up.

However, next day I had to explain precisely why my sink was hanging off my wall at such a crazy angle. Home Sister fixed me with her beady eye. 'So, nurse, you were saying about opening the windows?' 'Ah, yes, Sister,' I went on, innocently. 'Well, it was like this: I put my foot on the sink to get up to open the window as it was stuffy and, well, the sink just gave way …' Sister peered at me critically for a moment. 'It's a considerable amount of weight to put on such a small sink,' she said, pointedly. 'Yes, Sister,' I said, thinking, *'Sweet Jesus, I'm for it, now.'* After another long pause she said, without looking up, 'Well, kindly stop using your room as a climbing frame from now on, nurse.' And that was it. She had bought my story, I think, particularly as I had a reputation for being a bit of a clumsy twit. This scene with Sister was recounted to my friends, over yet more Woodbines and Merrydown, and to the accompaniment of yet more giggles, gasps and 'Oh, Mary's' later that night.

1952, the year I hit Putney, was also the year that the first espresso coffee machine came to London. It became 'cool' to frequent coffee bars, which were thought to be almost illicit dens of iniquity and heinous vice. In Putney there was a wonderful coffee house called Zeta's, which was a large shop on the corner, where we would all go on our day off. There was also Mario's, a lovely old Italian place, that did huge knickerbocker glories, which I thought were marvellous. We would sit there, nursing a coffee in a Pyrex glass cup and saucer, and someone would put music on the Wurlitzer, and it all seemed very sophisticated and grown up to be out alone, spending my own meagre earnings on coffee, Woodbines, cake, ice cream and music. We were always hungry, always thirsty, but we had to live within our means, which were very tight, so there was no other way.

Of course, I loved shopping. Window shopping, mainly, as I had little money and none to spend on clothes. Putney High Street was a broad, posh, leafy road, with lovely shops, and I liked nothing better than to stroll up and down it, lusting after goods. I remember longing for a pair of red stilettos in Saxone's that cost £3.00 and wondering how long it would take me to save for them. I knew I would have to save for weeks, even months, as, in those days, if you didn't have the money, you simply didn't have something you wanted. You had to 'save up' and that could take ages and ages. I thought '*I'm going to have those*' and, eventually, after weeks of saving hard, I did.

I liked fashion a great deal. Back home I had been used to my mother being able to run up anything. She made my fabulous pale strapless green evening dress, which I wore at sixteen to my first grown-up dance in Clonmel, which doubled as my leaving 'do'. In those days you had one good frock, and one good pair of strappy evening shoes, and they lasted you for years, too. I brought the green dress with me to Putney, in the hope I'd have occasion to wear it one day, and I was always amending it: putting some ribbon on it here, or a corsage or bow, or a little flourish, there. It's what we did in those 'make-do-and-mend' post-war years.

I also bought my first proper two-piece suit in Richard Shops: it was pale grey with a pleated skirt. It was all the rage to have big skirts with net under-petticoats, and to wear gypsy-style blouses on top. Everything was waisted and girly, and I knew I looked good as I had a tiny waist back then. It would all be topped by having a 'shampoo and set' at a new, modern hair salon on the High Street, which had those dome hairdryers we sat under in rollers (although this would only happen on very special occasions). I would have to save for a cut and set, and would have one maybe every two or three months or so. Meanwhile, I would snip my fringe myself and, being me, it was usually lop-sided once I'd finished hacking at it in the bathroom mirror.

During these first few months of settling in, I would write dutiful letters home, making my London life sound busy and meaningful, and would make my job sound important (which it was to me). I certainly didn't tell of the men I saw naked, or the cigarettes and booze, or even what I had encountered on the wards. My mother would write back, telling of local and family news, but would ask almost nothing of my life in England or as a trainee nurse. She simply didn't want to know. This hurt me, but I knew how proud and stubborn my mother was. So I had to rely on my sisters for the real news from back home. I felt very nostalgic thinking of the lovely rural countryside, the orchards, and my dear sisters, brother and father, and the dogs, but I didn't miss either my mother, really, or the nuns. And of course, I never asked for money. I certainly knew I would never get any for wasting my time in that

'Godforsaken Protestant country', so I didn't bother asking. I knew that I had to make it on my own, and I was utterly determined to do so, no matter what it cost.

4

Bring Out Your Dead

Hospital life is all about disease, birth and death, so I knew, sooner or later, I would have to be dealing with all these things first hand. I was quite trepidacious, but also curious. Plus, after my disgrace of fainting away in the morgue, I had begun to get used to seeing all sorts of things on the wards, although we were usually given very menial tasks to do, which were still mainly about scrubbing everything in sight with carbolic and Dettol, or rolling up bandages, emptying bedpans, folding linen and mopping the floors. However, after a few months we were being given more challenging, albeit still fairly basic, tasks to do. Fairly soon after I started, I was on a stint of night duties, which was also all very new to me. In charge was a horrible woman, whom we nurses called 'the Beetle'. She was small, dark, with a tight bun, and she scuttled around, keeping us in check. We were terrified of her, and Sister Morten became 'the Beetle' thereafter: someone we always had to keep our eyes open for, but who would often surprise us by appearing and scaring the life out of us.

It's often the way that people die in the early hours of the morning, something to do with our bodily rhythms, whereby people reach a low ebb in the middle of the night. Thus it was I was confronted with handling my very first dead body one dark mid-winter night. It was three in the morning, and I was already feeling exhausted, when Sister came and told me that Mr Johnson had died. He was a retired ex-policeman, a nice old man with a big handlebar moustache, rather like Jimmy Edwards, the popular entertainer. That night I was on the ward with twenty patients, all of whom needed things like bedpans, fresh water jugs or more medication. The nurses would sit at the end of the ward at a little table with a light on, doing paperwork and keeping watch. It was quite a quiet night, until Sister came up to me and whispered, 'Nurse Powell, go and lay out Mr Johnson.'

The flowery curtains were already pulled round Mr Johnson's bed when I arrived on the scene, jittery as a kitten. I felt quite spooked by what I might see, and hesitated for a moment, feeling anxious. Luckily, the twenty other patients on the ward were snoring away, but I was alone, as the other nurse had gone on her 'lunch break' (which was a meal in the middle of the night). I was very nervous as I drew the curtains and saw him lying there, in the half light. I sort of half expected he might sit up and start talking, like in a horror film, so I watched him to see if he was really gone for a minute or two. There was no breathing, so that was it. Next, I had to wash him down, so I got a bowl of soapy water and a sponge, then starting at the top of his head worked my way down all the way to his toes. This turned out to be a very long way as Mr Johnson was about six foot five, with his huge bony feet hanging over the end of the hospital bed.

I felt so sorry for him having died that I started crying. I was uncontrollable. Poor old Mr Johnson, I was thinking to myself, dead and gone. His life was well and truly snuffed out. What would his family be feeling? Would they miss him? As usual the tears were flowing, and mixing with the soapy water as I washed and wiped away at his poor old body. I actually felt quite horrified by what I was doing. I'd never touched a dead body before, although I'd seen the headless monster in the morgue. I was curious at the icy marble texture of his skin and how his face had begun to sink in as his jaw slackened. I saw his eyes had sunk into his head and I shook involuntarily, feeling quite spooked out by it all. He now looked very different from the Mr Johnson who had sat up in bed while I took his temperature and pulse, only yesterday. There was an eerie silence in the ward around me as I washed my way down the poor old man's body. I noticed, slightly squeamishly, that he had started oozing from his orifices and I had to plug them with cotton wool as I worked. It felt so weird to do this to what had been a warm human being only a few hours earlier: he had been a sentient being, with a history and feelings. Now he was like a waxwork, although he'd never be an Araminta, I thought wryly.

Anyway, the worst part was to come, when I got to his middle, or rather, to his 'private parts'. I had no idea what to do at all. The poor man had a catheter sticking out of his penis and I had absolutely no idea how to get it out. There was no one around to ask, and I couldn't bear the idea of going to ask Sister, in her hidey-hole office, who would bite my head off as soon as look at me, so I got the rubber tube and started yanking, then pulling, then wrenching, trying to get the damned thing out. Poor Mr Johnson's body was going this way and that, and his head was bobbing up and down, in a very undignified way, as his willy was yanked hither and thither by me. I was desperate to get that tube out. I could feel my heart racing, while my mouth was dry, as panic was rising. I bent over the poor man's penis, and was examining the tube close up, yanking and pulling all the while, when I suddenly heard a fierce whisper hissing behind me, 'Nurse Powell, *what on earth* do you think you are doing?'

I stood up, red-faced, tube in hand, and Mr Johnson's body did a ghastly jump, led by his willy (which was still firmly attached to his catheter). I must have looked a total sight, tears still pouring down my panicked face, with my hands going all over his private parts. Sister stepped forward and got out her scissors on their little chain and neatly snipped the rubber tube and the catheter slid out, nice as pie. I stood open-mouthed, feeling such a fool. 'Next time, use your common sense, will you, Powell,' was all Sister snapped as she turned and left me alone again with the battered body. So undignified. I said sorry to Mr Johnson right there and then for all I had put him through, and cried some more tears of sympathy. I said a little prayer for his soul … and, of course, the other parts that had got a rude walloping from me.

Then I had to lay him out, which is what all of us nurses were taught to do, as preparation for being taken to the morgue. When he was finally finished, I called Staff Nurse to check him over. It had taken me an absolute age, since I had had to keep stopping to blow my nose throughout as I had found the whole thing traumatising. Staff came along briskly and emptied his locker of his worldly goods. There were a couple of packets of Woodbines in there, packs of twenty, which, amazingly, patients were allowed to smoke on the ward. Back then it was thought that smoking calmed their nerves … there was no thought of cigarettes being a health hazard; in fact, quite the opposite. To my horror Staff said, 'Let's take these Woodbines. His relatives won't notice,' and with that she pocketed them. I was amazed at her attitude, but I didn't object. I'd been in enough trouble for one night. However, I thought it was a very bad thing to do, and I didn't feel comfortable being 'party' to our crime. Yet, once we were on our break, and Staff got the fags out, I smoked a couple. I really needed a smoke after all that – I was gasping.

I think during that first year I was often naïve about the rules, or I failed to follow the strict regulations, as I was used to always trying to skirt round them back home. It was force of habit for me to be a bit rebellious, I suppose. Also, a means of survival. I tried to be good, and tried to be the best trainee that I could possibly be, but I had a mischievous streak and often acted on impulse or said things without thinking them through. However, I was still really desperate to prove my mother's prediction about me being hopeless and a quitter was wrong. I was not going to be sent home, tail between my legs. I was going to succeed: I had to, as it was a matter of life and death. Thankfully, some of the more experienced nurses took pity on me. Sometimes we spent hours hunched over the sinks on night duty scraping poo and vomit off sheets with our scrubbing brushes and bare hands, which got sore and rough. We were scrubbing and cleaning endlessly; one of my more experienced nurse friends, Beryl, used to joke that pushing the enormous floor mop would increase her breasts, so we all sang a comical 'I must, I must, I must increase my bust' with every strenuous bush stroke across the floor.

We would also spend hours folding linen in the linen cupboards, and if I was on nights it would get very warm and soporific in there. I had a pal, a third-year nurse, Sandy, who surprised me one night by clearing a space on the enormous second shelf (which was about ten foot long and two foot deep) and telling me to get up on the shelf, and lie down to take forty winks. 'No,' I protested. 'If the Beetle finds out, she'll have my guts for garters.' 'Go on with you,' Sandy encouraged. 'You're all in. Have an hour. I'll wake you up.' I could see she meant it, so I did. It became a regular occurrence after that when I was on nights. I'd clamber up, and be out in two shakes of a lamb's tail (as we used to say). Sandy would be shaking me and I'd be down a dark tunnel, back in Clonmel, trying to avoid the whack of my mother's large wooden spoon over my head. 'Get up, Mary, you lazy girl,' Sandy would be whispering. 'Time to get up – you've had an hour's kip.' For a moment I'd think it was one of my lovely sisters, Una, and then I'd focus on starched sheets and pillows in neat white piles, and it would all come flooding back to me. Sweet Jesus, I was in that linen cupboard. However, those snatched naps were a real life-saver.

Putney Hospital, being on the edge of Barnes Common, which was a huge geographical area, meant we got all sorts drifting in, night and day. Tramps, children, couples, basically anyone who had come to grief in the open air or on the road, some way or another, were brought in. The ambulance men (and they were mainly men then) were aware that I was a 'new girl' and sometimes took advantage of it, especially when I was left on duty in casualty all alone. Another bitter cold night in the middle of winter during my first year it turned out that I was the only nurse in casualty left on duty. It was sometimes like that, as we were often not that busy at night. Putney Hospital had been set up originally to serve the local community, so it was not a really hectic place serving central London, like Barts (St Bartholomew's) could be. It was part of Westminster Hospital, so we did send patients there when necessary, such as when a case was more serious or needed more complex equipment or nursing.

However, this evening Night Sister was at dinner and the house doctor had gone to sleep in the downstairs 'on call' bedrooms allocated to night staff. He could be called and woken up in an emergency, and Sister floated round the hospital at night, but I was supposed to cope the best I could with most situations, on my own, otherwise. When an ambulance turned up at the entrance the rule was that I had to go out to it and see who was being brought in. Usually the ambulance men would say, 'Got a heart attack here, nurse,' or 'It's a car crash,' or whatever. I think this night they saw me coming. It was freezing and I'd thrown on my cape, but was shivering terribly in the wind. The rule was I wasn't supposed to accept any patient without seeing them first in the ambulance. The ambulance men, George and Charlie, whom I'd seen before on nights, indicated that because it was so bitter cold they hadn't got the time or inclination to let me clamber aboard and check out their patient. I was also rapidly turning into a human icicle, so I went back into casualty as the two men carried in this fella on their stretcher all wrapped in a red blanket. 'Found him on Hammersmith Bridge,' explained George. 'Think it's a heart attack, probably.' And with that they were gone.

So I was stood there, next to this man, wrapped in a red ambulance blanket. He looked frozen, poor old chap. He had grey whiskers and bushy grey eyebrows, and was in a brown raincoat and suit. I folded back the sides of the blanket and thought, '*Sweet Jesus, he looks really terrible*,' so then I felt for his pulse. Nothing. I felt again, and then put my head on his chest, listening for his breathing. Not a sausage. *Oh my God! He was dead! Oh Lord, what should I do? Sweet Jesus, I was really for it now!* I looked around the casualty department and absolutely no one was around; it was like a ghost town, as it was now four in the morning. Thing was, the rule was I was not authorised to take in a dead body; it was absolutely against regulations. This had been drummed into us as trainees over and over and over again. Had I been listening? Well, obviously not.

I was supposed to go out to the ambulance and assess the patient, then if they were deceased they were termed Brought-in-Dead (BID) and I was supposed to decline them, so they went straight to the morgue, or even to another hospital altogether. We had been told many times that it was too much paperwork, as a BID involved the police, the mortuary, the coroner, tracking down relatives and so on. If they were found dead in the street or died in the ambulance they were never brought in. That was the rule. It was a huge job and we were not supposed to touch it with a barge pole. So there I was with a dead body on a trolley to dispose of – a poor old BID – and I hadn't the foggiest where to start sorting out such a mess. I could feel the panic rising: Who could I turn to? Where would I start? I pulled the blanket down further and saw his grey, frozen face with icy whiskery eyebrows. Dead all right. As a doornail. Jesus, what was I to do? In those days there was no resuscitation equipment, like defibrillators or anything like. I stood there, panting quietly – what on earth should I do next? I couldn't go and get Night Sister and say casually, 'Oh, by the way, Sister, I have a dead body in Casualty.' She'd absolutely kill me. So thinking quickly now, I wrapped him up again in his nice red blanket, so that he looked like a giant Christmas cracker on his trolley, and then pushed him into a corner, trying to hide him to buy some more thinking time. Suddenly I heard Night's Sister's clipped tones behind me: 'Any developments, nurse?' I jumped out of my skin. 'Sorry? … Er, no, Sister, everything's fine … This man … I don't think he's very well … actually, Sister …' But it was no good, Sister was already peering past me curiously at the red-wrapped bundle that I was desperately trying to hide behind me all the while.

I couldn't stop her as she advanced towards the stretcher. 'What on earth is this doing here? That's an ambulance blanket – why didn't you give it back when they brought him in?' And with that she pulled the blanket down: 'Jesus Christ, he's dead,' she said. 'He's not,' I said, covering wildly, 'surely not. The ambulance men just brought him in. I was just … I didn't realise …' 'Brought him in?' She was shouting now, and I could see her eyes beginning to pop out in their characteristic way. 'Nurse, you know that you are supposed to go out to the ambulance to assess the patient. Rigor mortis has set in – this means this man died two or three hours ago! He was brought in dead – B-I-D. You know better than this, Nurse Powell, or you really should do by now.' At her angry words my usual waterworks started flowing. I was soon crying helplessly. It was a nightmare; I was in trouble, all over again. I'd be back in Ireland in a wink, with my mother 'told-you-so-ing' me to my father over my head. 'For goodness' sake stop snivelling, nurse.' Night Sister was incandescent and she went on and on and on about procedures and rules. Then she went on and on about needing to uphold standards and follow correct regulations and what would happen if we didn't (the end of the world, obviously). Suddenly she marched off and got Percy the porter and instructed him in clipped, frosty tones to take the poor dead man down to the mortuary. She didn't even look at the body, poor thing, or try to work out who he was. What a way to end his life – I felt truly sorry for him. Then Sister was back, facing me, eyeballs popping: 'I'll see you in my office, Powell, ten o'clock sharp, tomorrow morning, *no nonsense*.' And with that, she turned on her heel and was off. Standing there, wiping my eyes, I realised that the ambulance men, as nice as they were, had pulled a fast one on me. I was a gullible greenhorn, a real eejit, and it showed.

So I was there next morning, exhausted and trembling, and it wasn't just Sister, but Matron, too, I had to face. I had to have a clean apron on, and stand, with my scrubbed hands behind my back, like a very naughty schoolgirl. Matron wiped the floor with me. 'You know there are rules, nurse? And rules are meant to be followed … blah-di-blah-di-blah …' I wanted to disappear between the floorboards. However, to be fair to her, she did stop and say, towards the end, as I was blowing my nose loudly, that she would have a word with Night Sister as I shouldn't have been left entirely on my own while I was training. So she was actually quite fair to me in the end, and I had to learn yet another painful lesson in the importance of sticking to the damned rules … My mother would have been so proud.

There was a more tragic death one night, however, which made me very sad and again made me realise how important it was to be thorough and observant as a nurse. A young lad of about fifteen was brought in after having a fall on the Common; it wasn't clear how, but he was probably larking about with some friends and had fallen out of a tree and broken his ankle badly. He was taken to the men's surgical ward, but mysteriously got worse, as he developed a very high temperature. His ankle was set, but still he worsened, and we discovered he was dying from tetanus (lockjaw), which was incurable at the time.

However, it was only when he was examined during the post-mortem that it was found that he had a deep graze on the back of his head. This has gone horribly septic and had done for him. It was appalling to us all that this injury had been missed. More importantly, it felt terrible that such a young life was snuffed out so quickly from something that should have been dealt with at the time, and which, today, would be so easily treatable with antibiotics. This kind of tragic incident affected me deeply, as I was only a teenager myself, and made me feel that life was somehow, sometimes, hanging only by a very fine thread. It also made me realise how important it was to be thorough in the medical profession, and how the smallest thing could turn out to be important, especially if it was neglected. This made me feel much more responsible, and assiduous, when dealing with wounds after this experience.

Sister Tutor, who was a very kindly woman, could see that we were deeply affected by this kind of encounter with death – a boy who had died too soon out of both an accident and human frailty. She would tell us that we would have to get used to seeing all sorts of things in our hospital lives, and that dealing with death was a major part of it all. Sometimes we would see things that would upset us for days, other times we'd see something that would stay with us for life. Even though some of the sisters and staff nurses were quite callous and hardened, and barely paid any attention to the dead and dying, they nonetheless respected that there needed to be a dignified way of dealing with the passing of life.

Helping people to die was seen as an important aspect of the job, and so Sister Tutor taught us how to approach it with human kindness and thoughtfulness. One day, shortly after the incident of the youth dying from the hidden head injury, she sat us all down and said, 'Don't ever let someone die alone. We didn't come into this world alone, and we should never leave this world alone. When someone is approaching their final hours it's so important to sit and be with them as they go, especially if they have no family.' Indeed, she taught us to sit and 'mop their brows, comfort them', she would say, 'hold their hands and soothe them'. She taught us to care, to spend time with people, to make them comfortable, to talk to them and to ease their passage into death. She was a wonderful, sweet influence and a nice woman, to boot, and her important lessons about something that had frightened me a great deal, at first, have stayed with me all the rest of my nursing life.

5

Yes, Matron; No, Sister

Putney Hospital was a totally matriarchal regime, similar to the Presentation Convent and, obviously, to my own family, where Mother Superior and my mother were both 'the boss'. Matron, who was a rather snobbish, upper-class woman, was at the top of the hospital's hierarchical tree, and lived on the job, day and night. She literally had a little flat upstairs in the hospital, with a kitchen, a living room and a bathroom. Sometimes Matron entertained 'at home' and we would sneak upstairs and try to peak through the glass in the door to see what was going on, like naughty schoolgirls spying on 'Miss'. We often failed miserably as we always starting giggling or lost heart or thought we heard the 'click clack' of Sister's shoes coming along the corridor which made us scarper, in fits.

Matron's life seemed to be entirely limited to the hospital, and, like the nuns, she always seemed to be there, on the job, with her watchful, grey eyes taking in everything, steering her large ship through the daily turbulent seas of hospital life. Her spacious office was right in the middle of the hospital, like the hub, and had an enormous wooden desk, a stripped wooden floor and a large grey plush carpet. Her windows overlooked Barnes Common, and Matron would sit with her back to them bolt upright, at her desk, in her large chair, looking very formidable. I knew that view out of the windows as well as the view back home from my house over the River Suir, as during my three main training years (1952–5), and qualifying year (1955–6), I stood on that carpet, in front of Matron's desk, numerous times, staring at her neat piles of papers, her pens in a pot and her small, white hands folded neatly in front of her on her blotter.

Matron was a compact, busy little woman, whom I feared totally. She was quite dumpy and plain and wore an extremely neat and spotless dark navy uniform with a pleated skirt (no one else wore this style). There was no apron but there was a little crisp white hat, perfectly folded, pinned to her iron grey, tight curls. She had white cuffs and collars and always looked utterly immaculate. Matron wore no make-up, of course, but would peer at me through her round wire-rimmed glasses, perched on her somewhat beaky nose. Whenever she looked at me, I would feel intimidated straight away, as if I had done something terribly wrong (I usually had, to be fair). It was so uncomfortable that it reminded me exactly of the sort of penetrating glare I would get from Sister Margaret or Sister Angela, when they were reminding me that God could see into my terribly sinful, blackened soul. Or was rather like the glare my mother would give me when I had scrumped some apples and had hidden them up my jumper. Matron and Sister Margaret, my mother and God all merged into one all-seeing, omnipresent eye, and somehow I was always its beady focus: I was always in the wrong and needing to do penance as a sinner.

Of course, I contributed to my own reputation for being a little bit giddy, a bit of a 'trouble-maker'. I didn't mean to, but I was always, somehow, the one to be up for a bit of a lark, or the one to be laughing loudest, or falling over something or dropping something, under the steely gaze of an older woman in starched uniform. One day, during our very first term, the kind nice Sister Tutor (she was the nicest one of the lot) was teaching us to dissect rats and mice. We were in the school room, which had foetuses in formaldehyde on shelves, which really disturbed me at first. And also good old Araminta laid out, with all her innards spread around her, ready for action. Being the class clown, I picked up one of the mouse's testicles with a pair of forceps and started off scampering round the lecture room, scaring the life out of the other trainees. I was just swinging them past the nose of a terrified Irene, another Irish nurse, when the usually calm Sister Tutor walked back in, alerted by the shrieks: 'Nurse Powell, what *are* you doing? You are here to learn, you are not here to amuse these girls!' She was red-faced with fury and I felt so embarrassed at being caught out, especially by her. It was supposed to be a bit of fun, but, as usual, I went just a bit too far. I was mortified to be in Sister Tutor's bad books as I badly wanted her approval.

On that occasion I got a good telling off, along the lines of 'You are here to absorb the serious art and craft of being a nurse, and you will have to knuckle down and do things properly, if you want to succeed.' Sister Tutor commanded our respect and would administer her own justice. She was usually right – and fair. Her word was law, and I respected her, so I would be straightened and would be saying a meek 'Yes, Sister,' to all of her edicts after any of my hare-brained escapades or mistakes. The other sisters were more scary, more punitive, and I was really terrified of them. Home Sister, who looked after the nurses' home, was the most scary of all. She could be nasty, and many a time I ended up not only in her office, saying 'Yes, Sister,' in a tiny little voice, but also I would then be moved on seamlessly to Matron's office, for the final ticking off, to teach me a lesson, to make me come to my senses, and so on. There I would be on the carpet, yet again, saying, 'No, Matron, I won't do it again,

Matron,' and then would creep out, tail between my legs, usually in tears and red-faced, well and truly scolded.

One of the worst night sisters was the Beetle, who was incredibly fierce and scary. She was a spinster, witchy like, and had a tight black bun at the back of her little round head, on top of a thin, bony body. She would literally rattle round the wards at high speed, at night, trying to catch us all out. One night one of the exhausted Dutch nurses climbed into one of the giant wicker laundry baskets and went to sleep. We tried to wake her up, and three of us were shaking her legs and rattling the basket when the Beetle scuttled into view. Of course, me being the tallest and the most voluble, I got it first: 'Powell, whatever are you doing? Stop that immediately.' It was only when she peered into the basket and saw a bundle of legs and stocking tops that she realised there was a nurse buried deep within the mounds of dirty linen and towels. As a consequence, we had to create our own 'early warning' system when we were on nights. We would scatter some granulated sugar along the corridor and we would relax until we heard the crunching and knew Night Sister was coming. Then we would hiss 'It's the Beetle' and jump to it, smarten ourselves up and look very 'busy' once she scuttled into view. Once she arrived we'd all look very innocent, folding towels, smoothing beds or writing on charts or tidying up. However, true to form, she was constantly picking on us: 'Nurse Powell, that bed is not made properly. Change the sheets and do it again,' and I would know better than to say anything other than 'Yes, Sister,' and go to it. I knew better than to argue – and I don't think I ever saw her laugh. I'm not sure if she knew how.

I was always in fear of both Matron, the Beetle and Home Sister, but some of the nurses were made of stronger stuff. One of my friends, Jenny, was a third-year trainee, a tough Northern Irish girl from the rough end of Belfast. Being a third year, she was older than me, obviously, and she told me a lot about how to survive the hospital regimen. Her family had had a real tough time during the war years. I liked Jenny; she was great fun, and we often tried doing new hairstyles for each other, talked endlessly about clothes (we both loved fashion), and what we would buy if we ever came into money or saved enough, as well as boys (I hadn't had much experience of them yet), and who we fancied at the pictures. Jenny and I also talked a great deal about the issue of the huge sense of responsibility that came with training as a nurse and how we felt about it all. Both of us had been the youngest rebels in our families, and we both had spontaneous natures that could get us into trouble. Jenny was a senior, in her final year, and couldn't care less. She'd had a back-street abortion (she confided one night over the

Merrydown), as she was a real one for the men. She couldn't resist, especially after a few drinks. My eyes opened wider and wider as she told me her amazing stories about her life and loves.

Anyway, Jenny and I also smoked liked chimneys. She liked her Woodbines, as did I. One night, in the sluice, we were cleaning out bedpans with scrubbing brushes. Always a lovely job. I was still a greenhorn and struggling to do everything right, but Jenny was quite rebellious by now, and used to bucking the system, and I was amazed to see her light up a Woodbine whilst we went on to the next horrible job of scrubbing poo, vomit and wee off some sheets. It was a disgusting job as they smelt to high heaven and we had to do the work with carbolic and elbow grease. I felt like retching several times over. Anyway, I just stood there open-mouthed at her smoking on the job, and looked around, terrified someone might come in and find her – smoking was completely forbidden by nurses, despite the patients being able to smoke on the wards. I thought '*She'll be in for it,*' and I was right.

We didn't hear her coming, but suddenly the Beetle appeared in the sluice behind Jenny. 'Nurse, you are smoking!' snapped the Beetle. I held my breath and waited for it, but Jenny didn't miss a beat. She carried on rinsing her sheet under the tap, fag hanging out of her mouth at an angle, and said, 'Yes, I fucking am.' Well, I nearly fell through the floor. For a start I'd never heard the 'F' word said out loud before, let alone heard a nurse say it – and let alone heard a nurse say it to a superior. I expected the sluice ceiling to come crashing down on our heads, or a lightning bolt to come shooting through the windows and take off Jenny's head with a single blast. The Beetle was silenced momentarily. I dared to peek up at her from under my lowered eyelids and all I could see were her eyes popping out of her head with apoplectic rage. I thought, '*Sweet Jesus, the Beetle will kill her now.*'

'You're to go straight to Matron's office, nine sharp,' hissed the Beetle through clenched teeth, her eyes like burning black buttons. 'Put that thing out right now and get back to work.' And cool as a cucumber, Jenny finished her rinsing, put the fag end under the running water and threw it in the bin. Then she dried her hands and sashayed out of the sluice deliberately slowly, turning to wink at me mischievously as she passed. I thought the Beetle's head was going to explode right off her shoulders there and then, she was that furious. I was frozen to the spot, as I'd never seen anything like it and had a secret admiration for Jenny's guts. 'Stop gawping, Powell.' The Beetle's ire was now unleashed on me. 'Get back to your work this minute, and let this be a lesson to you.' 'Yes, Sister.' I knew better than to answer back, but I wasn't sure, exactly, which lesson I was supposed to be learning. Later, after her carpeting, where she was grounded for a month, Jenny said to me with a wicked wink, 'Don't let the fuckers walk all over you, Mary. Learn to stand your ground.' I think this edict became my motto over the next sixty years, and I never forgot Jenny as she was a damned good nurse, even though she was a rebel.

There was a constant tension between meeting the needs of the regime, so that rules were followed and things were done perfectly, and meeting the needs of the patients, who needed time, nursing and care. The kind sisters and staff nurses were the ones who understood, like Sister Tutor, that we nurses needed to spend a bit of time with people, making them feel comfortable, relating to them, comforting them as well as doing the usual things like taking pulses and changing dressings. This was an aspect of the job that I really loved, and wanted to do. But this had to be counter-balanced against the needs of keeping things constantly clean and spit spot, and there were sisters who were real dragons and staff nurses who were total pains. At first I was horrified by some of the diseases I encountered. Things such as diabetes, which had side-effects, like gangrene or blindness, meant the poor people (very often men) suffered terribly. There was often nothing that could be done to cure them, back then, so I felt it was my job to make the patients feel as comfortable as I possibly could. And they were often grateful for any little spark of human kindness to relieve both their symptoms and their boredom.

I remember one dear old boy, a Mr Jones, who was in his sixties and totally blind. He was in the men's medical ward when I was in my first year. He had a bit of Brylcremed hair combed over on top and a big fluffy moustache, and used to smoke a pipe (amazing to think of this now). He used to sit up in his stripey blue and white pyjamas and call me as he heard me go past, 'Nurse, Nurse, put a bit of baccy in me pipe, would ya?' Or he'd say, 'I was wondering if you was on today. Fill me pipe fer me, will ya, m'dear?' He couldn't see a thing, poor man, so I'd sit on the chair next to his bed and fill his pipe for him. But as I'd be doing it, Staff Nurse would come along and snap at me, in front of him, 'Powell, what are you doing? There's bedpans to empty. Get a move on, nurse.' 'Yes, Staff,' I'd say, but be seething inside as I felt sorry for the old bloke – it was all the pleasure he had left in the world. When she'd gone, Mr Jones would whisper, 'Sorry I got you into trouble, girlie,' and I'd say, 'Never mind. Enjoy your pipe, Mr Jones.' I'd feel like it was the least I could do to give the poor old man a break from his misery. I thought Staff was behaving like a bitch at the time, but I had to hold my tongue (unlike Jenny, I wasn't that brave, yet). It didn't stop me filling Mr Jones's pipe for him, though. I felt it was the least I could do.

When I met Staff in the corridor afterwards, I must have looked angry, as she came up to me and said, pointedly, 'When you've been here as long as I have, nurse, you won't be fussing over him like that.' I opened my mouth to argue with her, but checked myself. 'Yes, Staff,' was all I said, but inside I felt upset. The poor old geezer just wanted a bit of baccy for his pleasure and it seemed so mean not to help, so inhuman. Some of the other nurses were very hard, but I have to say I was always a bit of a softie, and I was often in tears over the state of people. I guess the reason I wanted to be a nurse was my compassion for their suffering. However, I could always hear my father's voice in my head teasing me: '*Oh, there she goes again. Her bloody bladder's in her eyeballs, crying over everything.*'

However, some of the trainee nurses found out during our first year that nursing was not for them. Some of them took to the profession because, like me, they felt they had a vocation to follow, while others had sort of fallen into it, or were pushed into it by circumstances beyond their control (like poverty) or family pressures, and really struggled with the whole thing. There was one of my friends,

Wendy, who had been a ballet dancer earlier in her life, and was very glamorous and beautiful. She had decided to train as a nurse because the ballet world had a short age limit, and she knew that by the time she was in her twenties she would be past it. She needed to find a way of earning her living as her family wasn't well off, and had thought that nursing might be it. However, right from the start it was clear she was not really cut out for the life of scrubbing toilets, emptying bedpans and taking temperatures.

On our days off she was always the first out of the Nurses' Home, dressed up to the nines, and on her way 'up West' as we called it. This meant a long double-decker red bus ride up to Piccadilly and then hitting the coffee bars in the West End of London, especially round Soho. Hanging out in coffee bars was very daring in those days, as they were full of 'Beatniks', young men in Sloppy Joe sweaters down to their knees, and with beards, longish hair (over the ears, anyway) and horn-rimmed glasses. Wendy would whisper to me, while she put on her red lipstick, 'Christ, I'm fed up with this boring place,' and she'd be off to find intellectuals and arty types in dives like the Macabre, a famous coffee bar in Wardour Street that had skeletons on the walls and coffins as tables. Wendy was no more a nurse than I was a policeman. Inevitably, she soon met a suave publishing type 'up

West', Peter, and it became a full-on wonderful romance (she told us over the Merrydown at night). Indeed, Wendy was always falling in love and clambering into our lodgings, through an open downstairs window, late at night. But now she was telling me that Peter was 'the One', or so Wendy thought. Very soon Wendy disappeared and got married, and Sister 'tutted' at the waste of time she had been as a trainee. It was heavily frowned on by the sisters to give up your training before you had finished, a real letting the side down. Yet there was a tinge of envy at finding a man, and having the option of making a family, as so many of the sisters and Matron seemed to be diehard spinsters.

Then another nurse, Linda, who was in her second year, ran off with the son of one of her patients. It was quite a scandal. Linda, who was a nice middle-class girl, and who hated nursing as well, had met Nigel on the women's ward, quite by chance. He had been sitting, dutifully attending his mother, who had had a hysterectomy and was fairly poorly, and it had been love at first sight. It was like something out of a romantic film or novel. Nigel was a ski instructor in Austria, and his mother lived in a very opulent flat in Putney. He had come over to visit her, and Linda could not help drifting past his mother's bed every five minutes to see if she was all right, to check her pulse, to tidy her bed or rearrange her flowers – when actually her main quest was to keep flirting with Nigel. Linda was very pretty, and not cut out for nursing at all, and it became clear that Nigel was really coming to the hospital to see Linda rather than his mother by the end of the first couple of weeks.

However, the sister on the women's ward at the time was not happy at all with this development. She liked her nurses to be nurses, to be obedient and disciplined, and totally focused on the job. Sister was increasingly enraged at the obvious flirtation that was going on around Nigel's mother's bed. We tried to warn Linda, but she was so besotted with Nigel that she didn't see the warning signs and she wouldn't listen to our warnings, either. Sister was a real old cow on that ward, one of the most horrible women I had ever met (and that's saying something), and she soon had it in for Linda. She knew that Linda would want to rush off at the end of her day shift to meet Nigel, who would wait for her at the end of visiting hours (and her shift), so Sister kept placing more and more obstacles deliberately in her way. It was as if Sister was jealous of Linda's handsome boyfriend – and so she exacted more and more obedience from a nurse who was rapidly pulling away from the hospital regime. Battle lines were drawn.

One night, at eight o'clock, Nigel was waiting outside for Linda, having said goodnight to his mother, who was gradually on the mend. Linda was finished for the day and just clocking off, when Sister said, 'Brown, before you go, check the cutlery in the kitchen.' The sisters always called us by our last names, just like in the army. It was very formal and made us jump out of our skins. 'Yes, Sister,' said Brown, obediently. There was nothing else she could say. She had to trot off and count out all the knives, forks and spoons in the kitchen drawers and then put them all back again, in the right order. It was a right palaver. (All the wards had a little kitchen off them, which housed all the crockery and cutlery for the patients – and this is what she was having to check.) It was now ten past eight, and Nigel was still outside, pacing up and down in the freezing cold. 'Goodnight, Sister,' said Linda. 'Not yet,' said Sister, pointedly. 'Check the sluice is tidy.' Linda bit her lip and hesitated. 'Yes, Sister,' was all she could say, and then went and checked it over, and came out five minutes later.

Still Sister was not finished with Linda. It was a nasty cat playing with an innocent, pretty little mouse. I was watching all this, out of the corner of my eye, thinking, '*Sweet Jesus, Linda is going to explode in a minute if Sister goes on.*' 'You haven't been in there long enough, nurse – how could you have possibly checked everything?' said Sister, getting more nasty and narrowing her eyes. I remember looking at Sister's lips, which were very pursed, set and tight, like a cat's arse. I was also watching Linda, who was flushing red now, and glancing anxiously towards the window, where Nigel's head was still bobbing backwards and forwards, as he paced, his breath on the air in little white puffs. It was now eight thirty, and the poor man had been waiting for half an hour in the ball-freezing cold. Sister was testing Linda to the limit of her endurance, as indeed this particular sister tested all of us on a regular basis. It was supposed to be character building: the stuff good nurses were made of. We were all supposed to say 'Yes, Sister,' or 'No, Sister,' or 'Three bags full, Sister,' to her every request, no matter how barmy or cruel.

I could see Linda was furious, rapidly reaching her limits, and also near to tears. On this last night it became clear, very soon, that Linda had had enough. Sister was following her around with her eyes and trotted after her into the sluice where Linda was mopping down the giant sinks for the third time. 'Don't skimp on the disinfectant, nurse,' sneered Sister, sadistically. With that Linda snapped and she suddenly picked up a huge red bottle of glycerin and thymol, pulled open the door to the balcony that faced a brick wall, and smashed the whole thing up against it, most dramatically. Liquid and glass flew everywhere. 'Nurse!' shouted Sister indignantly, but it was too late. 'I'm out of here,' screamed Linda, pulling off her apron and her hat. 'I'm going now, I'm leaving, and I'm never, ever coming back! You can't stop me, either!' And with that she ran out to the waiting arms of Nigel, who was still hoping patiently for her to arrive outside. Sister looked totally shocked, but turned straight to me and barked her orders: 'Clean this mess up, nurse – jump to it, and make a good job of it, or there'll be trouble.' And with that she turned on her heel and marched out. 'Yes, Sister,' I whispered, but was inwardly both deeply shocked and a bit delighted at what I'd observed.

Needless to say, Linda went off and married her handsome Nigel; she never did come back. After that, they lived in two rooms together, locally, for a while, and I would see her all glammed up doing her shopping in Putney High Street. We all thought it was great, and we were all definitely a little bit envious. She'd had enough of nursing, very quickly, and she'd escaped – we thought it was so brave of her to stand up to Sister. She had got her man, and a new life, and we wondered, to ourselves and over our cider and fags, whether we ourselves would ever meet 'the One', and if we did, if we'd have the courage to follow and not finish our training. I felt, secretly, that I really wanted to finish and that men seemed to be quite a bit of trouble really, even though I was fairly naïve at this time. Eventually, Linda went off to live in Austria with Nigel, and had three children, and, as far as I know, lived happily ever after having an absolutely wonderful time. Sister, on the other hand, told us in no uncertain terms that Linda was a 'bad lot', a hopeless nurse and not a good example at all to us trainees. We all said 'Yes, Sister,' but inside we were cheering Linda on for going after her own happiness single-mindedly, rather than being a dutiful, but bitter, slave, right to the very end. I, on the other hand, wanted to stay on my chosen path and didn't think I was in danger of any white knight coming my way soon to rescue me from my chosen profession.

6

Of Lice and Men

As a trainee I had to spend time on all the different men's and women's wards: medical, surgical, geriatric and then children's. I had to learn to treat all sorts of conditions and understand many curable and incurable diseases, while constantly dealing with the basics: cleanliness, hygiene, nursing care, nutrition and rigid hospital rules. During my training I also had to learn to 'suture', which meant doing minor operations and procedures on patients, usually in a side room that was specially set up for it. Nurses were expected to be able to do stitches – which was actually sewing the patients' flesh together with a needle and catgut – or to assist a doctor if they were doing something more complicated. The idea of minor surgery was that it could deal efficiently and quickly with something like a laceration or other semi-serious injury without having to take up valuable time in the operating theatre.

Of Lice and Men

One evening a young girl, of about five, Susan, was brought in by her rather distressed father. They had been out on the Common and she had fallen over and cut her knee very badly. It looked like she had fallen on some broken glass (of which there was lots around, due to people drinking beer or lemonade out of glass bottles), and she definitely needed some stitches. She was fairly hysterical, and clearly frightened about having stitches done. This was my first time, so I was terrified of getting it wrong (my usual response to having to do any new tasks), and I had a particular fear of making a mess of it, especially after my years of being tortured and criticised by Sister Margaret and her bloody Bride of Christ knuckle-duster. However, the task was at hand, and I had to do it, and I had practised many times on poor old Araminta, so it should have been fine. I knew that there was a doctor on call, should anything go wrong, plus Staff or Sister hovering about somewhere nearby, should I get into serious trouble. I felt I was ready to begin, and I thought to myself: *'Go on, Mary, you can do it!'*

The minor operating room had a high couch in the middle, for patients to get up on, and large sluice-type ceramic sinks along one wall. There was a little portable trolley on wheels made of metal and glass, and the ubiquitous steriliser in a long cupboard in the corner of the room, bubbling away as ever. The father, who was a very nice man in his thirties, lifted his poor little daughter up onto the bed, and I could see she had a really nasty deep cut on her kneecap. She was keeping her leg straight to stem the bleeding, but was crying the whole while, with her daddy standing with his arm round her weeny shaking shoulders. I thought, *'Sweet Jesus, I'd better get on with it.'* I went and got my instruments and wheeled them over on the little metal trolley to beside the couch, ready for action. We persuaded little Susan to lie down; she was pretty scared of the whole procedure, but I approached her as cheerfully as I could and tried hard to put her at her ease. To give her courage, I got her dad to stand next to the table as I started wiping her knee with cotton wool and antiseptic, after washing my own hands thoroughly (just like I'd seen Sister and the surgeons do, many times).

Dad was just saying 'There, there' to Susan, when he glanced down at her knee, which was now a yawning, wide-open wound from her leg moving about, with blood flowing freely. To my amazement, he went down like a ninepin, right on the spot, and fainted right away. There was an almighty 'crack' as he descended to the floor, in a heap, and Susan stopped crying and started screaming 'Daddy! Daddy!' I told Susan to straighten her leg and hold on, while I rushed round the bed to where he was lying and saw, to my absolute horror, that blood was pouring voluminously from his head. *Oh my Christ. What on earth had happened?* Then I realised that as he went down he'd hit his head on the sink edge, which was a sharp and unyielding corner, and had actually cut open his own skull, very badly by the looks of it. 'Staff!' I shouted at the top of my voice. 'Emergency.' A few seconds later both Staff and Sister arrived. They might be dragons most of the time, but in an emergency they could be utterly brilliant, and I was actually relieved that they were there for a change.

The poor old dad was out cold, and his blood was still pouring, and puddling onto the floor. Meanwhile, Susan was beside herself with fear and was crying uncontrollably. Then two ambulance men arrived on the scene and got Dad onto a trolley and suddenly we were into a completely different scenario. Susan's dad was taken down to X-ray and, to my great consternation, we found out soon after that he had actually fractured his skull very badly, from ear to ear, right round the back of his head. Sweet Jesus, those sinks were bloody unforgiving. Meanwhile, poor Susan was still in the minor operations room, with me, and I was struggling not only to calm her down but finish off her stitches, which seemed insignificant now. Ironically, because of the emergency with her father, I managed to do them fairly easily, without any problem at all, all the while thinking, '*Sweet Jesus, what are we going to do now?*'

When I was done, Susan and I went down to X-ray, with me reassuring her all the way that Daddy would be fine, only to find out that her father had been rushed over to the Atkinson Morley Hospital for emergency surgery. Susan had no idea what her home address was, or her surname, and we had no idea if they had a telephone (few people had them then), but she probably wouldn't have known the number, if they did. No matter how much we asked her, Susan couldn't articulate anything useful, especially as she was still so upset and calling for 'Daddy'. Plus, she was now abandoned to Putney Hospital and to my care. So there I was, stuck with this poor traumatised child, and her father had been carted off with a fractured skull to somewhere else. All this drama had stemmed from a few stitches to a knee cut, which should have been a routine procedure. Of course, all this happened before mobile phones or other easy communications were available, so the only thing to do was to get the police. A friendly local plod arrived and sat down with Susan and tried to get her to describe where they lived … and eventually he took her to the local police station. I found out later that they did locate the mother, and that the father survived and was actually fine, thank goodness, but was in hospital for quite some time after. However, it was a lesson to me to think about how other people react when they see blood, or have to deal with trauma affecting loved ones. And it certainly made me learn to think on my feet. Later on in my career I would often find men would keel over at the sight of blood, or the sight of a needle, so I usually made sure they were sitting down before I began any of my medical ministrations.

It was soon time for another stint on nights. I always found these shifts very hard work, not least because of feeling incredibly tired and hungry in the early hours and how lack of sleep affected me in the days afterwards. My experience of the B-I-D (Brought-in-Dead) incident and my carpeting by Matron ('Nurse, you know what the situation is, and what the consequences will be, if you make such silly mistakes') had made me much more wary. So this time, when the ambulance arrived, I made sure I bothered to put on my navy cape with its red lining, and went out to see what George and Charlie had for us. It was raining hard this night in particular, with a bitter cold wind, but I was absolutely not going to get caught out again. Or so I thought. The ambulance men had picked up a tramp on Barnes Common: this was not uncommon (as it were) as we got them drifting in all the time. There were loads of homeless men after the Second World War, who had been demobbed and not got jobs, so often they were military men with drink problems, who had nowhere to go. George said the man probably had 'hypothermia' as he was icy cold and sodden, but that he was still breathing (thank God). So I felt his pulse in the ambulance, and it was extremely weak, but, yes, he was still alive. He had long straggly hair and a beard, with terrible breath, and was in rags and looked a bit like Jesus Christ, so I thought I couldn't really turn him away – who would know what would happen if I did? (I imagined more lightning bolts aiming straight at my terrible, sinful head.)

George and Charlie wrapped a couple of red ambulance blankets around him, and brought him in on a stretcher, moved him onto a waiting trolley and left swiftly. Meanwhile, I went to get the night doctor up, a Dr Thomas, who was a bit of a weasel. I had to go to the sleeping quarters and knock on the door. I managed to rouse him and he put on his white coat over his blue and white stripy pyjamas, and slung a stethoscope round his neck, while half asleep and grumbling. I knew I could only get him out of bed on pain of death, literally, as Dr Thomas did not like to be disturbed. He could make your life a complete misery. However, I could see that the poor man on the trolley was in a bad way, and I certainly didn't want yet another death in casualty on my tender conscience. I knew he was heading off the cliff rapidly towards death, as he was so weak and cold, so I absolutely had to go and get the doctor up, whether he liked it or not. (At least I was following that procedure correctly, I thought to myself.)

Casualty was a big, bright cream and green room, with all these stainless-steel sterilisers bubbling away, full of instruments, down one side of the room. We had to sterilise absolutely everything, and then take the instruments out when they were wanted by the doctors with a pair of Cheatle forceps. Everything was boiled to oblivion in a big silver steriliser in boiling water. Anyway, a very grumpy Dr Thomas had gone over to the man on the stretcher, to start examining him, while I was despatched to go and sort out some fresh instruments. I was just checking they were ready, and was opening the steriliser lid, with the steam hitting my face, when I heard 'Jesus Christ' emanate from across the room from Dr Thomas. My first thought was that the tramp had died meanwhile and I had another dead body on my hands – it was beginning to feel like the Keystone Cops, where I imagined I would be wheeling yet another trolley round the corridors playing hide and seek with the red blankets for scant cover, under Matron's omniscient gaze.

'Nurse!' shouted Dr Thomas. 'Come here, immediately.' Oh, Lord, I was for it. So I rushed over and tried to look demure (and failed). 'Did you look at this man?' I blinked, as innocently as I could, and said 'Yes'. Sweet Jesus, what was it now? Dr Thomas was in no mood for me being meek, I could see. 'What?' 'Yes, Doctor, I did,' I said more boldly. Dr Thomas straightened up and looked at me with disdain. 'Well, did you notice that he's bloody walking with lice?' To illustrate his point, Dr Thomas pulled down the red blankets and I looked: I saw suddenly that this man, who was about seventy, was moving everywhere. His wet, ragged clothes and his tangled, greasy hair were covered with little moving things. He had lice in his eyebrows, his ears, his nose, his hair, his lashes, his collar, his hands and nails; absolutely bloody everywhere.

I looked imploringly at Dr Thomas: 'Oh God, what are we going to do?' 'It's not "we", nurse, it's "you", for a start,' snapped Dr Thomas, bristling at me. 'First, you're going to shut your mouth, and, second, we're going to admit him,' said Dr Thomas. 'He's still alive, so we have to treat him.' I looked down at the moving mass, and nearly fainted. What would Sister say? If the Beetle saw this I'd be skinned alive. I was horrified. 'Where are we going to put him?' I could hear my voice was getting higher, becoming more of a strangled squeak with every question. Dr Thomas was tired, irritable and fed up with me, so he started off in his usual patronising tones: 'Look, if you have an emergency case you put them in the middle of the ward, in a bed, so that's what you are going to do.' I looked down at the hairy, dishevelled heap on the stretcher under the red blankets, which were beginning to heave. Dr Thomas looked for a moment, then yawned. He moved away indifferently, saying over his shoulder, 'But he'll have to have a bath first.' 'It's two in the morning,' I said, horrified. 'How can we do that?' Dr Thomas rubbed his eyes and yawned again. 'Well, that's your problem, nurse. I'm going back to bed.' And with that he ambled off in the direction of the sleeping quarters, stethoscope slung over his shoulder, coat undone, leaving me entirely alone and in charge of the poor old freezing, infested tramp.

I looked at this great lump of lice-riddled man under his red blankets and racked my brains: *What on earth was I going to do with him? Thanks, Dr Thomas!* My patient was a big, heavy man and I gave him a bit of a push on his trolley, and it hardly moved, so I could see it was going to be quite a job. His eyes were closed, and he was the colour of chemical sludge, so I pulled the blankets round him so he looked like a large red sausage, with just a big veiny nose sticking out. I held my breath as I looked around Casualty – thank Christ it was pretty quiet, and there was no sign of the Beetle anywhere. She was whom I dreaded most: if she scuttled into view, her keys rattling, her shoes clicking, her beady eyes picking up everything, I knew I'd be for it. I had to act fast.

So I tiptoed along, wheeling my crawling quarry, up to the men's medical ward and tracked down my Irish friend,

Carrie, who was also on night duty. I hovered at the end of the ward and waved to her at the desk. 'Psssst!' I whispered. She looked up and smiled at me, but I gestured to her, frenziedly, to come over and put my finger up to my lips to denote 'hush'. 'I've got a problem,' I whispered maniacally as she arrived, and blurted out the whole scenario, hoping she didn't look too closely at my patient. All the time I was wondering if he was about to pop his clogs as I was doing nothing to raise his temperature yet; it was only mine that was going through the roof. Carrie rolled her eyes heavenwards. 'Why are you always doing it, Mary?' 'I don't know, but what was I to do?' I replied, groaning. 'Why does it always happen to me?' Carrie was exasperated, but being a pal she could see I really needed help. Part of the unspoken code between us nurses was that we helped each other, no matter what, if we could. We were in the same boat, as nurses, and we had to pull in the same direction, together. It was the only way we could survive the hospital regime.

Luckily things were quiet on her ward that night, so she slipped away and together we rolled Mr Lousy into the bathroom, which was a huge white tiled room off the side of the ward. 'I'll have to keep an eye on things,' Carrie whispered. 'I've got a full ward, and a couple on the way out.' 'Of course,' I said, desperate that nothing would take her from me, as I had no idea how I was going to handle my man alone. We manoeuvred the trolley next to the big white bath that was in the middle of the room. It was an old-fashioned type of six-foot-long ceramic bath with huge brass taps one end, and it had big feet (rather like me, I thought) and high sides. Carrie pulled back the top red blanket and I heard a little scream: 'God, Mary, he's crawling.' I bit my lip, and could barely look. I put on the taps full blast as we had to get him into a warm bath as soon as possible. He had hypothermia and it was already three in the morning, which was a vulnerable time if he was going to snuff it. The water had to be warm, not too hot, as we had to warm him up gradually, literally thaw him out. But time was running out, and he was almost unconscious: he was still frozen and getting paler by the minute. We put loads of liquid Dettol in the bath, so it stank to high heaven, but it was the only way. We just worked against the clock all the while, and I asked Carrie if the Beetle had been round yet. Apparently she'd done her rounds an hour ago and wouldn't be back until five, so we still had a bit of time left, luckily.

The tramp's clothes were absolutely filthy. I'd never seen anything so disgusting in my life. They disintegrated as we pulled and cut them off, layer after revolting layer. And, boy, was he alive alive-oh, with lice almost as big as beetles crawling over everywhere. We got some newspaper and wrapped up his clothes, thinking they'd go straight into the hospital incinerator. He had a few coins which we put on the side. Apart from that he had nothing on him – just a pencil stub, a bit of baccy and cigarette papers. Finally, he was stripped and he was all filthy skin and bone. His skin was impregnated with dirt, in deep stripes, and was very hairy, which the creepy-crawlies obviously loved. What a warm, stinky habitat to nest in. We did a one, two, three, heave together and got him from the trolley into the deep, warm disinfectant bath, with me holding him under his smelly, skinny armpits and Carrie at the black feet end. The lice were running riot now: running over the water, up the sides of the bath, and as he hit the suds they started pouring out of his hair, his ears, his armpits and his pubes. The water began to turn black; it was a nightmare.

Undaunted, and still with an eye on the clock, I poured liquid soap solution on his head and started scrubbing. Carrie started at his feet, doing the same. We scrubbed and we scrubbed, and worked our way along every inch of his poor old, bony body. His pubes were dancing with the beasts; Carrie got there first and I heard, 'Yuk, Mary, this is absolutely disgusting.' I had to agree, although I couldn't speak, as I didn't really want to open my mouth (just in case something got in there). After twenty minutes the water was so dense with dead lice we pulled out the brass bung which was the plug, and refilled the bath again, with warmer water this time. Carrie nipped into the ward and checked on her patients, while I took my man's pulse. He was warming up a little, but his pulse was still faint – however, a bit better than before, and he was still alive. His eyes were closed, as he was in a semi-comatose state; he was very heavy to move around and I had to keep him from sinking under the water. Meanwhile I filled up the bath again, and repeated the scrubbing process: scrubbing, rubbing, de-lousing and sudsing. Carrie came back; no dead bodies on the ward, either, as yet, thank God. We got a comb and started to comb through his hair and beard, and out the lice marched again – there was an endless supply, or so it seemed – were they multiplying on the spot?

We let out the brass bung and filled up three times in all. I was glancing at the clock endlessly, and hoping against hope no emergency would come in, or the Beetle would take it upon herself to do a spot check, which she could do sometimes, to catch us all out. If she did it tonight I'd be for the high jump, all right. I cursed and cussed Dr Thomas under my breath, as he was snoring away downstairs, not having to do any of this gruesome task. Eventually Mr Lousy was pink and clean, fresh as a newborn babe (well, almost). The bathroom looked like a tidal wave had hit it. We managed to get him into fresh, clean blue and white stripy pyjamas and even combed his straggly grey hair and beard. I was tempted to cut it, but there was no time left, so it would have to wait. Carrie mopped up the floor and I got the red blankets and bundled them into the bathroom laundry basket, which was a giant rectangular thing on wheels. The laundry was taken out every day, so I knew it would be removed in the morning by the early shift staff. We wheeled our newly scrubbed tramp out into the middle of the ward, which had an empty emergency bed in the middle, at the end of the patients' meal table. It was there precisely so patients could be brought in in the night without disturbing everyone. We could hear the snorings, mutterings and fartings of the men, always a nightly cacophony, and still no one woke up. Carrie turned down the sheets, and we got hold of my man – we did a 'one, two, three, hup' and he was soon tucked in, looking totally angelic. Jesus, I was exhausted. I took his pulse: it was better, now regular and strong.

Then together Carrie and I went back to the bathroom, which still looked like a bombsite. So the next job was to scrub and disinfect every single inch as we had to remove all evidence of our nocturnal 'crime'. There were pools of water and dead lice everywhere. 'You owe me one, Mary,' said Carrie, good-naturedly. 'I owe you, big time,' I said, somewhat relieved. 'The Merrydown's on me tonight.' By eight in the morning everything was tickety-boo and Mr Lousy was sleeping peacefully, still looking quite beatific in bed. We'd done it; so I hugged Carrie with thanks, clocked off, went back and collapsed into a deep, dreamless sleep of the dead.

Suddenly I was woken up by a loud rapping on the door. *What on earth?* The door opened and in came the maid, looking worried. 'Mary, wake up. It's the telephone.' 'Uh?' was all I could manage. The maid shook my shoulders and pulled down my sheets. 'Mary, it's Sister, on the phone in the hall for you. Mary, wake up. You need to come to the phone. Now!' 'Urgh, wassatime?' I had absolutely no idea where I was, what day it was, what was going on. 'It's ten o'clock in the morning – come now.' I was supposed to sleep all day, so I was totally disorientated being pulled out of my deep sleep. Reluctantly, I pulled on my pink candlewick dressing-gown and slipped on my pink slippers and went down to the office. I was deep asleep, but was soon very awake, once the voice of an irate Day Sister hit my ear. 'Come straight back on the ward, Nurse Powell, this instant. I want to speak to you immediately.' 'Yes, Sister,' was all I could croak out. Oh Lord, I was in for it. I had to go and put all my uniform rigmarole on, yet again, including struggling with my damned hat, and I'd only had a couple of hours of sleep. I felt like death warmed up (rather like my tramp).

When I got to the men's medical ward Day Sister's face looked like absolute thunder. I wondered if Carrie or even

Dr Thomas had told as they were the only two who knew what had gone on in the night, under cover of darkness. I was carpeted in Sister's small side office, and stood there, hands behind my back, like a naughty schoolgirl, swaying with exhaustion. I could see she was furious as her eyes glinted behind her glasses as she spoke: 'You are responsible for having an emergency bed in the middle of the ward, are you not?' I nodded, helpless under her rapier-like gaze and interrogation. 'Where's the blanket he came in?' I couldn't see where this was going, exactly, so I said meekly, 'In the linen basket, Sister.' She stood up and marched off in the direction of the door, throwing it open quite dramatically, and telling me to jump to it. I followed her meekly outside. When we got to the linen basket she lifted up the lid and I thought, *'God, I'm in for it now.'* 'Look in there, Nurse Powell.' I peered in and, to my utter horror, the two red blankets were still crawling, and now everything else in this huge linen basket was alive, too. 'You do realise we could all get lice now, don't you, Nurse Powell? And we could all get nasty diseases from these little beasts.' As it sank in, I wanted to sink through the floor, too. 'What on earth were you thinking?' I stood there, mortified. 'How could you contaminate all this linen?' Thing was, I hadn't thought. I imagined the linen basket would be whisked away, first thing, but obviously someone had looked in and brought it to Sister's attention. It was the fatal flaw in an otherwise brilliant plan. I had nothing to say, but the tears started, as always. Sister was beyond irate. 'What *are* we going to do with you, Nurse Powell?'

I opened my mouth to tell her about Dr Thomas and the position he'd put me in. What was I supposed to do? I started with 'But, Sister …' and Sister silenced me. 'No "ifs" or "buts", Nurse Powell. You know full well that you could have got someone down to Casualty and you could have washed the patient down there. You needed to do that so you didn't transmit his disease to the rest of the hospital.' 'But Dr Thomas said …' But Sister stopped me again. She did not want to hear that Dr Thomas had told me to set up the emergency bed in the ward; she didn't want to hear any excuses and certainly no nurse was allowed to say anything against a doctor. They were gods. They were to be obeyed. Their word was not to be questioned. And we lesser mortals had to sacrifice ourselves on the altar of duty. I'd been here before, many times. You would have thought I'd learned my lesson by now. 'Procedures are procedures, and that is that, nurse, else where would we all be?' 'Yes, Sister,' I replied, groaning through gritted teeth.

Next morning I was back on Matron's carpet at ten in the morning. I felt there should be a little spot on the carpet that said MP on it, like those Hollywood stars' pavement handprints you saw in the magazines. I seemed to be standing there so often, I ought to offer to get a new carpet, in case I wore this one out. My mother had taught me how, luckily. Meanwhile, Matron was snipping at me, in her posh, tight tones, as ever: '… and it shouldn't have happened, nurse, and you need to be more observant in future.' I felt her eyes on me for a moment, as I was examining the colours of the rag-rug: red, green, blue, orange and yellow. 'I don't want to see you in my office again, Nurse Powell,' she said ominously. 'It seems to be a little too frequent for my liking.' I left the room sobbing, and made a beeline for the Nurses' Home. It was hopeless; my mother was right. I would never be any good; I was a useless, careless, sinful girl. I'd soon be back on that plane, with my mother gloating, and sent off to Dublin to be trained by the nuns. I'd never make it here. As I was blubbing down the corridor I bumped into Sister Tutor. 'What's the matter, Nurse Powell?' Out it all came: Dr Thomas's attitude, the almost-dead tramp, the lice, the scrubbing, the linen basket, the carpeting. I was a mess and I didn't think I could make it as a nurse. I said, 'What can I do, Sister Tutor? I want to do a good job, so why am I always in trouble?' Sister Tutor really surprised me then, when she said, very kindly, 'Listen, Mary, when you've passed your exams – which I am sure you will – you'll make a wonderful nurse. You have a good heart. You just have to learn from your mistakes, and you have to keep going.' I looked up at her and couldn't believe my ears. I blew my nose loudly, and she laughed. 'I know you'll get there in the end, of course you will.' I could have hugged her and jumped for joy, but I knew better than to try.

7

Public Enema Number One

One of the most amazing things about Putney Hospital at this time was that, although men and women were segregated, patients with all sorts of conditions were lumped in all together, so you'd find failed abortions next to appendectomies, or cataracts next to mastectomies in women's medical; or in men's medical, diabetics (who were incurable then) next to men who were constipated, or those with 'growths' of all sorts, such as in the lungs or the prostate (what we'd now call cancer), who were beside stomach ulcers (which were mainly treated by drips full of milk). The surgical wards would have broken femurs next to car crash victims or brain surgery. Then there was the children's ward, which was boys and girls, and geriatric, which again was segregated into gender. The main wards were often a real nursing challenge as there were mixtures of patients with a variety of needs, who were in for something that was relatively trivial, like tonsils, next to people who had cancer and other incurable diseases. Another thing that was typical of the time was that patients stayed in bed for a long time in hospital and were 'confined' to bed, so they had to use bedpans for wee and poo. Today, we are used to people going in and out overnight for operations, and being up straight afterwards (due to what we know now about thrombosis risks), but back then people stayed weeks, even months, in bed, until they either healed or died. So we nurses got to know the patients over a long period, and even became friends with some of them. No wonder some of the nurses and patients fell in love, as there was time for a real relationship to develop over a few weeks, or even months.

So the idea of bed rest was also very important, and with few miracle drugs, patients had to be nursed, often to the end of their lives, through painful illnesses, with often very limited pain relief administered rigidly. There was no TV, and visiting times were limited to a strict hour a day. Relatives could not stay over then, so even when someone was dying they had to go home. Some wards were beginning to have radio, but the boredom was tangible. There were no mobile phones, obviously, although there might be a pay phone, but it was on a trolley and difficult to use, there was no privacy and you had to have the right change to make it work. More often than not people had no one to talk to for hours at a time. So we nurses would talk to them, find out about them, listen to them, especially if there were no relatives or friends around at all. Patients might have a newspaper, magazine or book to read, or some board games, like draughts or dominoes, but if they were very sick they weren't really up to concentrating. I found it very hard to see people suffer, and I always did my best to relieve them with a joke or a kind word; it didn't take a minute to be cheerful, but it could often change their day and made me feel better about the job of dealing with the incurables, especially. Befriending a patient was part of the job, and they often got spiritual help from the father or vicar who would come round the ward, and talk to them. The Salvation Army would even come into the ward and play to people, especially if they were near the end: it was a way of sending them off, or helping them to rally or cheering them on, if they had turned a corner medically. Basically, the hospital was a small community, a microcosm of the world outside, and in those days we were supposed to provide all sorts of help, emotional and spiritual, as well as purely physical. That was what nursing was all about (and what I still think it should be about): care.

* * *

I remember there were operations then that were quite barbaric and that now would take no time at all, or wouldn't even happen, as they have largely gone out of fashion. In the early 1950s tonsillectomies were all the rage, as King George had had one, and everyone wanted to follow the king and his family. It was believed back then that the removal of the tonsils got rid of all sorts of upper respiratory tract problems, so children, and even adults, had them all the time, especially after endless bouts of laryngitis or bronchitis. To be honest, when I got to Putney I was aghast when I first experienced an English pea-souper fog, or smog, in the winter, and it was absolutely impossible to see any further than my nose (not even that far when it was bad). I thought the smog was probably the cause of all the coughing, spluttering and sore throats that were prevalent at the time (along with the Woodbines and other rough cigarettes we all seemed to smoke). The air was so much cleaner and fresher back in Ireland, or so it seemed. Anyway, people came into Putney Hospital for their tonsillectomies, and then they would have to lie in bed for about two weeks at least to be nursed afterwards. It was a fairly tough operation, where the surgeon used a 'tonsil snare' like a cheese cutter to remove the tonsils, and the adenoids (which were behind the tonsils), and there would be masses and masses of blood from the procedure. I remember one patient, a woman in her forties, Mrs

Baker, had swallowed loads of blood during the operation, and then she was vomiting it all up for ages afterwards back on the ward. It was quite disconcerting to see all this blood coming out of her mouth – it reminded me of the TB I had seen back home, which involved a lot of vomiting of blood. And it seemed incredibly painful for her to be sick after having her throat cut on the inside; she was groaning in pain and looked terrible. Poor Mrs Baker couldn't speak, poor thing, or swallow easily, so I had to spoon-feed her, tiny teaspoons of gruel (thin porridge), or jelly or soup, bit by bit. It took ages to get anything down her, but it was what we nurses did. There was also a high risk of post-operative infection, so we would be taking her temperature and pulse all the time. Today, these operations have largely gone out of fashion, I know, as the tonsils are thought to be quite useful in stopping bacteria going down into the lungs. Also, their removal is thought to be quite an unnecessary operation (and there is always a risk from anaesthetic). But if the operation is done, it's in and out in a day, or just one night in hospital, but no more than that. Plus, nurses don't seem to have time to give their patients a drink of water (let alone sit and feed them), if what I read in the paper is right. But back then nursing meant nursing, care meant care.

The other operation that was just coming in on the NHS, and was also quite challenging, was the cataract operation. I didn't see many of these, as it was quite experimental then, but a patient would be in a side room, off the main ward, and would have to be in complete darkness, lying down, flat on their backs, for at least a week after the operation, which used general anaesthetic, not local. We would have to 'black out' the room, just like in the wartime, and make sure no light came in at all. Then they would be forced to lie down, flat out, with no pillows, and simply not move. This was so utterly boring for them, but it was essential. They had real stitches in their corneas back then which had to be taken out by the surgeon after the operation by hand, so they were not allowed to move their eyes, or react to light or move their heads. We had to bed-bath them, and feed them very gently, by lifting their heads slightly off the bed, and keep them hydrated. We also had to lift them onto bedpans, their bodies still largely flat, so it took a nurse each side of the bed. It was intensive nursing, and quite a to-do. Amazingly today having a cataract done is like going to the dentist: you are in and out in an hour and half, spit-spot, just like that. But back then it was a very risky operation, and quite experimental, and it took a lot of intensive caring from nurses to deal just with one patient.

* * *

When patients needed to be 'isolated' they were often put out on the balconies, outside the huge, tall windows that lined the wards. This was called 'barrier nursing', as we sometimes had to make sure the patients did not come into any contact with other patients. It could be pretty grim for the patients. Other patients, who might be near death, would be put in side rooms, but there was a limited number of these rooms available on each ward. The idea of 'barrier nursing' was to try to prevent disease, and to try to isolate infection, so that it would fail to spread. The use of penicillin had really revolutionised nursing in the post-war years, but it was still in fairly limited supply. There were some diseases that were still rife and that were deemed incurable. Venereal disease was widespread after the war, as the men came back from all the far-flung corners of the world, having had all sorts of exotic and erotic experiences. Of course, it wasn't something that was spoken about openly, but I got to see some things on the men's medical ward that really opened my eyes and shocked me. Syphilis, a horrible venereal disease, seldom talked about or acknowledged, was incurable back then. There was a lot of it about, but as the 1950s progressed the antibiotic treatments got better and the fatalities started to decrease. But when I started, in 1952, it was still rife and common for men to die of what was then a shameful and really nasty illness.

Public Enema Number One

A Mr Jones was brought in to be barrier nursed and I soon discovered he was in the third stage of syphilis. This meant he had gone through the first stage, of having a painless sore on his private parts; and then the second stage, which was more flu-like symptoms, with rashes and headaches, and with weight and hair loss. The third stage was the most dangerous, and fatal, with the nastiest symptoms, affecting the nervous system, the eyes, heart, skin, blood vessels. Basically, by the third stage, which could be long and painful, the body was beginning to shut down and the patient on their way to an inevitable death. All we could do was give Mr Jones Streptomycin, and nurse him well and hope for the best. It wasn't going to cure him, as it was all too little, too late. Quite often these kinds of patients left their symptoms to develop for far too long, often due to being ashamed of how they got the disease in the first place, or, as in the case of many men, they failed to go to their GP, and just put up with the symptoms until the illness was firmly embedded and sadly untreatable. It was tragic, as it was socially unacceptable and a source of shame to really acknowledge you were sick this way, so many men died unnecessarily at the time.

Mr Jones was a nice, good-looking man in his forties. He was polite, and clearly educated, and he told me he'd been in the army during the war. He read books all the time, but as I nursed him I saw his body slowly rot; it was becoming hardened and black. I'd never seen anything like it. I had to change his dressings one day, and I was unwrapping his feet to re-bandage them. I was horrified when I got down to his skin, which was like black, lifeless cardboard. As I unwrapped the bandages a couple of his toes came off in my hands. I was utterly aghast, and felt sick, although I tried hard not to show it. He didn't say, or seemingly feel, anything, as he had already lost sensation in his feet – there was no circulation or nerve endings any more. It was terrible. I watched Mr Jones endure a long, slow, painful death with extreme fortitude. He absolutely didn't complain, and said 'Thank you, nurse,' politely, for everything I did. I would wash him, feed him and try to cheer him up. He liked doing crosswords and he'd ask me for help with the answers to two across or fifteen down. He knew it was hopeless, yet he endured the unendurable with quiet dignity, and also he had virtually no visitors. I wondered if his wife had left him when she found out, as he didn't seem to have a wife. I felt, in a way, relieved as I wondered what wives did when their husbands got these kinds of terrible diseases. Did they know? Did they get it as well? How would a couple talk about it, especially if the man had been away during the war, and the woman didn't know what he'd really been up to? I had never nursed a woman with syphilis; it was nearly always the men. But I guess women must have got it, obviously, especially the poor old street girls or 'prossies'. I was very disturbed as I watched Mr Jones fade away, painfully and slowly, and it made me feel very cautious about taking risks myself sexually (not that I was anywhere near that yet, even in my late teens). Anyway, Mr Jones bore his disease bravely and with dignity until I came in one morning and found his bed was empty and being hosed down with loads of disinfectant; it had taken him about nine weeks to die a long, horrible and painful death.

On a lighter note, we were learning all the time 'at school' more detail about the nursing profession and practice. Sister Tutor was a great teacher, a really kind and lovely woman, and we had regular hourly 'chalk and talk' lectures, with pictures that she pointed to with a wooden stick, and pickled specimens, to examine. She had practical sessions of dissection (frogs and mice mainly), and her talks were always lively and informative. We sat in formal rows at little desks, so it was like school all over again; I was often at the back of the class, larking about, and she would fix me with her eye, and give me the occasional sharp 'Powell!' remonstration. I always seemed to play the fool – old habits hanging over from my repressive schooldays, I suppose. But I liked Sister Tutor, and I respected her, so I learned a great deal from her. Then we would pore over heavy medical books, and spend hours learning anatomy and physiology names by heart: there was absolutely masses to absorb. It was all very technical and scientific, and I loved it. This was mixed with the 'hands-on' learning on the wards, which was, at first, observation, and a lot of scrubbing and cleaning. Then, gradually, we were unleashed on the unsuspecting patients, and were allowed to do more ourselves. We were instructed first, given measurements and quantities, but once we got on the ward, with real, live people, we were largely on our own, and it was quite terrifying – especially at first.

One day, during the first six months, I had to learn to give an enema. This was another job, along with my first injection, that I felt very anxious about administering to real, live patients, properly. Enemas were somehow incredibly personal, and intimate, and I hoped to put it off as long as possible. However, the day eventually came when I could avoid giving enemas no longer. I was on night duty and Sister came up and told me to give Mr Brown an enema as he had not 'been' for a week. Nurses and doctors were always concerned with patients 'going' because being 'regular' meant that everything was in working order. Because people were stuck in bed for so long, being static and not active, 'going' became very important and bowel movements were monitored daily, along with temperatures and pulses. Sister would stand at the bottom of a patient's bed with her clipboard, and say, 'Have you gone today, Mr Potter?' as if she was saying 'Pass the finger sandwiches' at a bridge club. She would write down the gruff 'yes' or 'nah' that followed on her clipboard, and then smartly move on to the next bed without any expression on her face.

I obviously knew the importance of regular bowel movement for health, as it had been drummed into me by Sister Tutor, so I went along to see Mr Brown, who was in his sixties and very constipated indeed. I had no idea really how to give an enema, as this was during my first few months on the wards. It had been explained to us, in detail, by Sister Tutor, but actually administering an enema for real was a completely different thing. I knew we had to boil up all the leftover bits of soap with water, and make them into an enema liquid. This was then put into a long, cylindrical glass bottle, and pumped through a long rubber tube into the backside of some unwilling patient. If I had had to do this to a woman it would have been bad enough, but to a man, and an old man, to boot, who was the age of my father, well, it was the worst job I could think of having to do.

Anyway, Sister had issued her edict, so I got all the equipment together and took it over to the bedside of Mr Brown, who was deep in his *Sporting Life*. He took one look at me, and at the long rubber hosing and the cylinder of liquid, and he knew exactly what it was for. He was a real old rough diamond, from the East End, a balding, rotund man, and he just said, 'You ain't gonna put that in me bum, nurse, not on your Nellie.' I realised straight away that I had a fight on my hands: I was public enema number one. So I started explaining to him that it was very important that he 'went', that this was a normal procedure and that it would help him. Mr Brown refused, point blank. 'I ain't having it, nurse, and that's that.' I tried all the health and common sense avenues, to no avail, so then I went the sympathy route, and told him I was always in trouble one way or another, and this would only make things worse for me. 'Sorry, dear,' he said, hardly seeming sorry at all, 'no can do.' And he went back to reading his newspaper. End of.

Suddenly Sister arrived. Luckily it wasn't the Beetle, but it was another day sister, Grainger, who was middle class and very strict. I was wringing my hands and was so worried now about failing at the task, I thought I was for it, yet again. Sister swished back the curtains and stood there for a moment, eyeballing Mr Brown. He carried on reading his paper, nice as pie. 'Mr Brown,' Sister said loudly, and he lowered his paper and looked at her over the top. 'Mr Brown, you need to roll over,' is all Sister said. 'Wotcha gonna do, Sister?' said Mr Brown, innocently. I thought it was like watching a prize fight between two champions and I wasn't sure who I was going to put my money on, at this point. Sister watched Mr Brown for a moment, and then she leant forward and said to him, in her posh, cut-glass, English voice: 'I'm going to shove this up your arse, Mr Brown, and I don't want any nonsense.' Well, I could have fallen through the floor at this extraordinary pronouncement, and Mr Brown's jaw dropped with utter surprise. Such 'common' language coming from a sister, and in such polished tones, was a revelation. I wanted to giggle helplessly and I stored it up for the girls later, while biting my lip. However, without further ado, Mr Brown, like a lamb to the slaughter, rolled over and presented his bum. I was utterly astounded. We pulled his pyjamas down and Sister stood as I fumbled about with the hose and liquid, and inserted the tube into poor old Mr Brown's rear end. He grimaced as the tube hit his rectum, but complained not a word. He took it like a man. Sister watched me, critically, and then disappeared, leaving me to administer the enema as best I could. It was not an easy job to do, and certainly not a pleasant one, but once Mr Brown had succumbed he sort of went with it, thank goodness.

It was customary for Matron to do her rounds of the wards twice a day, morning and late afternoon. She would arrive, just like clockwork, and in the half an hour before her inspection was due we would all be ushered out to clean and sweep, tidy and organise, and make sure everything was just tickety-boo for Matron's visit. A couple of days after I had administered Mr Brown's enema I remember being on the ward when Matron visited. She was a small, neat, bustling woman and she marched up to the bottom of Mr Brown's bed, accompanied by Sister and me, that day, and took hold of his clipboard attached to the bottom of his bed to read the notes. I remember her being all smart and tidy, with her little hat tied perfectly under her chin with a bow, and her pleated skirt and black shiny shoes: all just so. I explained to her that Mr Brown had had an enema to deal with his chronic constipation. 'Well, how are you now, Mr Brown?' asked Matron, as if she was at a dainty ladies' afternoon tea party. Mr Brown answered Matron, without looking at me, and said: 'I'm all right now, Matron – I've had a bloody good clear-out.' I thought I was going to burst into fits, but Matron didn't blink; she just said, incredibly politely, 'Oh, I'm so pleased, Mr Brown. I'm so glad you're feeling better.'

There were always plenty of characters on the wards. I remember a dear old man called Mr Poysner, a Cockney who had big pebble glasses and who smoked a pipe all day. He probably had something like prostate cancer, although we didn't call it that then. He'd say 'I can't piss' if someone asked him what was wrong with him. 'It's me old waterworks,' he'd say simply. Mr Poysner had a tube going into his bladder (at least I knew what a catheter was now, and, more importantly, how to get one out), and it leaked all the time, so his bed was always getting wet, poor old fella. I was constantly changing his sheets, and had to put a rubber sheet under him, in order to preserve the mattress. I also gave him blanket baths, which was a way of washing a patient in bed, from head to toe, without getting them out of bed. I had to bring along a bowl of warm water, a flannel, soap and towels, and it would be a meticulous daily wash, including a close wet shave with a Sweeney Todd style of cut-throat razor. His bed-baths were important as poor old Mr Poysner was constantly having his 'wee' accidents.

He was a sweet old geezer who called all the nurses 'Gladys'. I think he'd probably worked on a street market or something. 'Morning, Gladys,' he'd say to me, and I'd laugh. I wouldn't correct him, as I knew it was his little joke. Or he'd say, 'Can you pass me baccy, Gladys?' And, of course, I would. He kept a stash of sweets and tobacco under his pillow, which we were constantly putting back in his locker, only to find it under his pillow again. Then, when his catheter leaked, the wee would seep towards his pillow and he'd be desperate to save his sweets and baccy: his little pleasures were very important to him, and I guess, being as sick as he was, he knew he needed to keep himself going somehow. I didn't begrudge it to him, at all. Anyway, one Sunday his grandson, Joey, also a Cockney, came to visit. Mr Poysner had been in hospital several weeks by then, and was slowly deteriorating. Joey had brought a pint of whelks, which was Mr Poysner's favourite treat. These were strictly forbidden by Sister, however, for some unknown reason. Possibly it was the smell, or maybe simply a class difference as it was traditional Cockney fare, not smoked salmon sandwiches. Mr Poysner had asked Sister if Joey could bring his whelks up, but she explained, in no uncertain terms, that it was not possible and rules were rules. I had no idea why he couldn't have his whelks – what did it matter, really?

I watched all this happening and I felt sorry for Mr Poysner. I'd got very fond of him by now, and I could see his grandson had made a great effort in bringing in a pint mug. Where was the harm? So I came up with a plan, which, God help me, I put into action. '*Sweet Jesus,*' I thought, '*I'm for it if Sister catches me,*' but I was determined to let Mr Poysner have a bit of pleasure, after all, as he had so little else. So I wheeled him out to the sluice, where there were big windows that opened onto the long, outside balconies. Then I whispered to his grandson to go downstairs and wait for me to throw something out to him. I opened the window and waited. When Joey appeared with his pint of whelks, I threw down a bit of rope, with a bucket on the end from the sluice, and got him to put the whelks in the bucket. Then I looked down the corridor: no Sister in sight. I came back to the window and hauled up the whelks on the end of the rope, out of sight of Sister. My heart was pounding, but I thought, '*Why shouldn't he have a bit of fun?*' We put the whelks on the floor in the bucket and I got him a little dish and he demolished the lot. He loved them. 'Oh, Gladys,' said Mr Poysner, with his eyes moistening, 'you're a bloomin' angel, you are. Gawd bless you, luv.' He ate his whelks with such gusto, it was very gratifying. He offered them to me, and I tried one out of courtesy, but it was cold, slimy and briny – a bit like snot, I thought – and really not for me. However, for Mr Poysner it was nectar of the gods and I could see the huge pleasure it gave him. His grandson was really pleased, too, as he was very close to his dear old grand-dad. Apparently, eating whelks in vast quantities was clearly a big part of the family tradition in the East End, especially on a Sunday.

All the while I was totally on edge, thinking, '*God, if Sister finds me I'll be for the high jump.*' I'd be twitching away, looking over my shoulder, keeping watch. However, during visiting hour things were usually quite quiet, and Sister would get on with her paperwork, unless there was some sort of an emergency. We did this trick with the whelks two or three times overall. Joey would arrive and signal to me he had a white enamel pint mug of whelks, so I'd disappear off to the sluice with Mr Poysner and get out my piece of rope which I stashed away in the back of a drawer. I felt like I was doing a real social service. I knew Sister would have murdered me if she'd found out, but she never did, I'm glad to say. However, dear old Mr Poysner died a few weeks after the last whelk feast. There was nothing that we could do about his cancer, as, again, he had left it very late and in those days it was a fatal disease. At least I'd done my best to try to bring him some pleasure and respite, despite things being so austere and hopeless overall. As a 'Gladys', I felt extremely pleased and gratified to have brought him a little bit of happiness with his baccy, sweets and, especially, his grandson's pints of whelks.

8

Letting My Hair Down

At Putney Hospital we all worked long, hard hours, five and a half days a week, as trainee nurses, and even when the work was done we would be studying and preparing for exams; or we'd be sitting in lessons with Sister Tutor or doing something unspeakable to Araminta for the umpteenth time. The camaraderie was fantastic, and despite the differences between us trainees, which basically centred on class, religion or nationality, we all looked out for each other, most of the time. Of course, there were squabbles, and minor jealousies, but on the whole we were all in the same boat, exhausted, broke and yet eager to complete our training and become proper SRNs. Naturally, we all wanted to let our hair down from time to time, and find a boyfriend … something only some of us seemed particularly successful at achieving – and I have to say it was usually not me.

Round the back of the hospital, on Barnes Common, there was an old-fashioned grass bowling green and we used to watch the local boys and men play in the evenings, especially when it was warm weather. Grass bowling attracted all sorts back then; it wasn't just an old people's game. We off-duty nurses would hang out the windows, sneaking a quick fag, and call out to the lads. It was a bit naughty, and if my mother had seen me she would have called me all sorts of names and pulled me inside, and would have given me a walloping, no messing. However, as nurses we were severely deprived of eligible male company, as there were very few male nurses back then, or at least none in our part of the hospital, and the doctors lived on another planet to us while the porters and other male staff were usually quite old or married (or both). So my best mates, Jenny, Hanse, Christe, Susan and I would gaze out the window in our spare hours, especially in the spring and summer, hoping to catch the gaze of some of the more good-looking young men. In fact, my friend Susan found herself a boyfriend, and then a husband, by luring him over from the bowling green to chat below our window, one summer's evening. There was much giggling and joshing as the boys chatted us up, and Susan and her fella would go down and smoke a cigarette together on the grass, and then she'd get on the back of his Vespa, and buzz off somewhere locally for a couple of hours for a drink or for a bit of innocent 'slap and tickle', as we called it then. There was no contraception available if you weren't married, and the only thing men could get hold of were horrible 'rubber Johnnies' or condoms, and it was something none of us nurses would talk about. The idea was to be abstemious or 'careful' (whatever that meant). Meanwhile, I'd watch wistfully out of the window, as Susan whizzed off into the sunset on the pillion with her beau, as I was absolutely sure no one would ever really want to whisk me away on the back of their Vespa for a bit of you-know-what.

I was very much an innocent then, on the sexual front. I'd had it drummed into me over and over, since the year dot, that things carnal were a mortal sin, and I had visions of the most terrible things that would happen to me if I transgressed. I had been brainwashed well and truly from very early on about the terrors of hell, and warned severely and regularly by my mother and the likes of Sister Margaret and the other tyrannical nuns, so the message went deep into my soul. Although I rejected so much of Catholicism intellectually (and also through my challenging behaviour, which was constantly at odds with the whole thing), the indoctrination of mortal sin went deep. I would be terrified of getting things wrong, doing bad deeds, getting into trouble and ending up roasting on a spit somewhere unspeakable. And yet, my rebellious, spirited nature meant that was where I was heading, no doubt at all. Plus, when it came to things like sex (I could hardly say the 's' word out loud), I found I had a deep reluctance to engage at all, despite temptations, due to all that had been drummed into me about sins of the flesh. It would take a great deal for me to be tempted into bed, or even into an extended frolic with a man, especially having seen what I had seen in hospital, by now, as a trainee nurse. The results of unprotected sex were not a pretty picture, I can tell you.

So I kept myself to myself pretty easily, and I wasn't really lured or allured – as yet. One of the first things I noticed, especially on night duty in the men's wards, was the men's blankets would be like little tents in the middle of the night or early morning. The first few times I saw this, I had no idea what on earth was going on – I was very confused indeed. It took a while until a wiser and older Jenny whispered in my ear what was going on, and I blushed red as a beetroot, to the roots of my hair, and exclaimed out loud, 'Oh, sweet Jesus, I'd no idea!' And I hadn't. I wouldn't have known an erection if I'd fallen over one (which I probably would have). I'd only just seen and handled my first penises, and they were always floppy old things belonging to fairly elderly or sick men. How on earth was I to know that men had erections in the middle of the night or early morning, and it was all an involuntary thing? I'd never been near an erection in my life, although I'd nearly pulled the penis off the poor old dead policeman Mr Johnson when I'd tried to extract his catheter during my first few weeks (which I shuddered to recall). When I talked to Jenny she explained that a lot of the men were having circumcisions in their thirties and forties as their foreskins were too tight, and they couldn't pee or make love properly. We were told to put Vaseline on the end of their penis and push it back down, and that was quite a job for an innocent, inexperienced Catholic-raised girl, I can tell you. I was embarrassed and they were embarrassed – it was red faces all round. No one had ever given me any proper sex education, and even as trainee nurses our knowledge was limited to very basic reproductive information, mainly looking at bunny rabbit corpses pickled in formaldehyde. The niceties of everyday bunny-free sexuality were far and away beyond me – so far.

However, we did like to go out and let our hair down, whenever we could. Of course, there was always the issue of getting enough money together. After paying Bert the porter for our Woodbines, we were often only left with a few shillings for snacks, clothes and entertainment. In those days there were no such things as portable radios (they didn't come in until the 1960s), and we certainly couldn't afford our own record players. There were those large wireless radios, in wooden boxes, that had to be tuned in, and we didn't have one in the nurses' home. Also no one had the money for a long-playing record player (that played vinyl), so the only places we could hear music and let our hair down was in a local coffee bar, like Mario's (which would have a juke-box), or even more wildly, we'd go out dancing either locally in Putney or Hammersmith (the Palais was famous), or even 'up West', to a big dance hall like the Lyceum Ballroom. In fact, it wasn't unknown for us to go up to town, and go round collecting the glass 'pop' bottles (like R. Whites dandelion and burdock, cream soda or lemonade) in a park, like Green Park, and then take them back to the grocers' shops to get the deposit money. We got two old pennies for each bottle, so if we were shrewd and worked hard we could pick up enough money to cover our dance tickets, drinks and bus fares all evening. (It was just like collecting the old scrumpy apples when I was a child and selling them to the local shop.) Anyway, we would eat some food in the local Lyons Corner House, which were popular cafés at the time, and take our dancing clothes in a bag, and then change and smarten ourselves up in the lavatories, so we came out fresh and ready to enjoy the evening. It wasn't the most salubrious place to get changed, but it was fun, and we always had a giggle doing it.

Sometimes the hospital would have a staff ball, in the summer and also at Christmas, which was fun, but the rest of the time we would go out on the town, locally. If it was a ball or a proper dance, out would come my one and only green strapless gown, which I'd worn in Clonmel at sixteen, and I would smarten it up with a new flower corsage or some sparkly embroidery. The same old dance shoes were worn over and over – in those days I had one pair and that was it, and I simply wore them until they fell apart totally in the end. If I was going out to a local pub or dance hall, I would wear a tight-waisted full skirt, sometimes with a big net underskirt, and my off-the-shoulder dirndl blouse, a short cardigan or bolero. I would 'set' my hair on rollers, put on red lipstick and powder, wear stilettos or court shoes, with my best seamed stockings, and feel like I looked a hundred dollars. Then we'd go out dancing, which was all the rage – it was the main way to enjoy yourself, and the main way to meet and get closer to a man.

We might go out once a week, if we had the cash, and all dressed up, we'd hop on a trolley bus (these buses back then were attached to an electric cable overhead by a long wire), and we'd go to the Hammersmith Palais. We would have our Woodbines to smoke, tucked in our little clutch handbags, but we would not be able to go to the bar to buy a drink; it wasn't really done then for a woman to approach the bar on her own. So we'd stand and smoke or sit and smoke, looking decorative, round the sides of the room, until a man would come up and offer to buy a drink or take us for a whirl round the dance floor. If someone bought me a drink, it would probably be a Dubonnet and lemon, or a gin and orange. This would be a drink that would last all night sometimes, or until the next man bought me one. It wasn't done for women to drink beer, certainly not pints; and wine was a rare drink, only drunk at Christmas or on special occasions and was very expensive. We only really ever had wine with meals back then, and in restaurants or for events like christenings, birthdays or funerals. So I learned to nurse a drink all evening if I had to, and most certainly would not have gone and bought in a round. Sometimes we would go into town, and end up going to a hotel along the Strand with the men we'd been dancing with all night, and having eggs and bacon at three in the morning, with tea or coffee, and that was very exciting. Again, we would need to get home afterwards, and also we'd need our beaus to pay, usually, as we weren't really up to hotel prices.

In the early fifties there were 'Teddy Boys' who wore sharp suits, with velvet collars, Brylcreme-slicked quiffs on their hair, like Elvis, who was just coming into vogue, wearing crepe-soled shoes and shoelace ties. They were always very smart and could be charming, if a bit rough. Also, there were ex-soldiers, and plenty of guys still serving in the forces; and local policemen and firemen, who were tough and muscly. And, of course, there were Beatniks, who hung out mainly in coffee bars, and who were intellectuals, and who preferred jazz (like Miles Davis) to the jitterbug. They were always in their 'Sloppy Joe' black jumpers, with their big, black square glasses and even grew their hair a bit (which meant it was over their ears. This was deemed long, and wild, in this 'short-back-and-sides' era). I preferred the Teddy Boys to the Beatniks, and overall was more interested in the men in uniforms than anyone else, if the truth be told. There was always something about a man in a uniform that was very attractive to us nurses. I think the same was true for the men; they liked us in our uniforms, too.

The off-duty policemen could be great fun. I met quite a few and they would dance me off my feet, amazingly. During my first year I met a very attractive policeman, a detective, and we went out once on a date. I always liked going to the pictures, and he'd buy me a box of chocolates and we'd go out to a pub for a quick drink afterwards. I was really keen on him, until he revealed he had a wife and two children at home, and I was utterly horrified, and had no intention of ever getting involved with a married man, so that was the end of that. Then one late evening he came into Casualty, with lacerated fingers from searching a criminal who had razor blades in his pocket. He needed stitching and dressing, and I was very annoyed and upset to see him, but had to treat him, as it was my job and I was on duty. Suddenly, he came over all charming and said, 'Why don't you answer the phone when I call?' Well, we only had one communal telephone in the nurses' home, which hung on the wall in the hall, and everyone could hear everyone's business. I said, 'You've got a nerve, as you're married.' He said, 'I'm not married any more,' and he looked at me imploringly. I thought '*Serves you right,*' and I bandaged him, but that was it as far as I was concerned. I wasn't interested, as he had already lied to me – how could I ever trust him again?

However, it didn't stop me going out dancing with my pals – it was the main way I let my hair down, how we all did. Unfortunately, the curfew at the nurses' home was ten o'clock, so my friends and I would have to start for home at nine thirty, which was ridiculously early and a real evening spoiler. The main aim was to find a man with a car who could give us a lift home at the end of the evening. Jenny was particularly good at picking up guys and she'd come up behind the back of the guy I would be dancing with and would do a triumphant thumbs up, signalling she'd found us a ride. Disgruntled, the men used to say, 'Why are you going so early?' or 'What's the rush?' However, we would not want to tell them we were nurses, because nurses had a reputation for being 'fast' (in other words, loose women). Nurses were thought to be free and easy on the sexual front, and we weren't. Or at least, I wasn't. I'm sure that's what my married policeman had thought; well, I'd taught him otherwise.

So we used to make up stories that we were secretaries working in a local firm, morticians or shoe-shop workers, or that we were visiting a rich auntie in a local block of flats or some other plausible story. I waited for the lightning bolts to descend on my head as I told these porkie pies, but I was amazed when nothing happened. Inevitably, we would be late for our curfew, and the off-duty policemen would offer a lift in their motorbike sidecars. These were fantastic – they were little covered pods, on wheels, with a seat for one person, which were built onto the side of a powerful police motorbike. I often found myself in one of these, at eleven o'clock at night, with no seat belt to put on (they didn't have them back then), roaring along the road, wind in my hair, towards Putney and Barnes. It was very exciting. However, I usually got the guy to drop me before I got to the hospital, pretending I lived in a local residential house, and that I worked nearby in the local shops or whatever. It's amazing looking back to see the lengths I went to make sure I kept up the story

– we were scared of the sisters' and Matron's reaction, and also scared the men would come and pester us and give the game away to Home Sister, who would go absolutely nuts. I would give my driver for the night a demure peck on the cheek, even a little kiss and cuddle maybe, especially if he was nice, but absolutely no more. I had to keep my wits about me, and I had my good reputation to maintain. I'd seen enough failed abortions to not want to go there myself, plus there was always the issue of mortal sin or hell and eternal damnation, hanging over my head like the proverbial Sword of Damocles.

Then it was an almighty scramble back to the hospital where a very goody-goody Irish nurse, called Kathleen, who always had her rosary clanking round her neck, would open the bottom window in the nurses' home so we could all clamber in late. Inevitably we'd be a bit tipsy and high on the adventure, and there would be a lot of 'sshhh-ing' and giggling as we all landed in a heap in Kathleen's room. By now Sister would be doing her late-night rounds of the nurses' home to inspect that everything was in apple-pie order, so we'd have to be quiet, and time our slightly drunken entrance impeccably, so we didn't get caught out. Sister would open bedroom doors and swing her flashlight into our rooms to check all was well. We anticipated this by stuffing our beds with pillows and our pyjamas, so it looked like everything was normal, and we were fast asleep, like good little nurses should be. If Sister had found out what we were up to really, she would have gone berserk, and we'd have really been for it.

One night we were really late back, and Kathleen had gone to bed, unable or unwilling to stay up for us any later. Hell, how were we going to get in now? We were all a bit tiddly, and it was decided, in a drunken moment, that the best way in was through a top part of a barred window that was open next to the front door of our nurses' home. It was a little top window that opened, and was actually in the downstairs toilet, next to the front door. This plan was not thought through at all, but seemed a good idea in a moment of drunken logic and sheer panic, about how to get in at this late hour. It was a mad solution to the problem of us all ending up being out all night roaming on the Common, and then carpeted by Matron in the morning. Anyway, for some unknown reason it was decided that I was the one to be hoisted through the window, perhaps because I'd climbed trees in Ireland, I don't remember why exactly. I probably volunteered, knowing me.

So Jenny and Hanse gave me a boost up either side, with me standing on their hands. The high top part of the window was open; it was pitch black inside, and I got half-way through. And then I got stuck. The problem was my boobs. I had large bosoms and once I was half-way through I got completely unable to go either backwards or forwards. Sweet Jesus, there I was wriggling and wrestling, with my top half squeezed into the building and my rear end hanging outside, with Hanse and Jenny trying to push me through, absolutely pissing themselves with laughter. And then I smelt something. It was horrible. A really nasty pooey smell. And then I heard groaning and moaning and the light flashed on and I tried to squeeze myself through the rest of the window, but was still stuck, when I looked down and saw, to my horror, that the on-call surgeon, a Mr Thurlow, was sitting on the toilet, beneath my hanging breasts, with his pyjama bottoms pooled round his ankles. He looked up at me, in complete shock, as I looked down at him, in utter horror. I turned my head to signal to the girls to stop pushing me, as I was only inches from the top of his head, but they didn't see what was going on inside, so they continued to push my rear end, so my breasts were bobbing up and down, just above his balding pate. 'Oh, Christ,' said Mr Thurlow, who slept downstairs in the nurses' home when he was on call. He looked up, and on seeing my boobs and head, quickly wiped himself and pulled up his pyjamas. 'What the hell ...?' The stench was terrible and he looked at me fiercely and just said, 'Bloody diarrhoea ... got the runs.' Before I could say anything he disappeared out the door, and then I could feel three pairs of hands dragging at my legs and then suddenly I was back on the floor outside, in a heap, with Jenny, Hanse and Mr Thurlow, all laughing their heads off helplessly. Mr Thurlow tried to straighten his face, but he was a good sport. 'You know it's one in the morning,' he whispered sternly. 'Get back inside before I report you.' 'Yes, sir,' we all chorused together in hoarse whispers, and then staggered up to our rooms trying hard to tippy toe. I never looked at Mr Thurlow in quite the same way again.

In the summer we'd also go out to the Roehampton Lido, which was a fantastic open-air swimming pool nearby (unheated, of course). We'd meet off-duty policemen there and spend all day, on a Sunday, chatting, flirting and sun-bathing. It was all very innocent, all very boy-meets-girl. It felt nice, as I felt free, and not under anyone's critical gaze, for a change. I also met loads of American GIs at the pool (there were a lot of them around back then), and we'd sit under the fountain and giggle together. There was one I particularly fancied, who was full of American chatter and charm. He would bring me stockings and chocolates, and seemed to have an endless supply of gin. He invited me to a party down in South London one day, and came and got me on his huge motorbike. I had dressed up in my best little lemon two-piece suit I had bought from Richards, and also my wonderful red shoes from Saxones, and I felt like the bees knees. I'd never been on the back of a motorbike before and I wasn't sure exactly what I was supposed to do. I got on the back, gingerly, and then he set off at a pace, so I clung on to him from behind like a little monkey as we whizzed and wove our way through the streets. Sweet Jesus, my heart was in my mouth, but it was an exciting ride all right. There were no crash helmets then, and I just clung on to him for dear life. When we got to the party I got off the bike and realised I'd put my lovely red shoes on the exhaust pipe, and the heat had blasted a huge hole through the sole. I had been so frozen on the bike I hadn't even noticed! I cried over those shoes, which my GI couldn't really understand, so he plied me with gin, and hoped, I think, to have his way with me. He spent most of the evening chatting to his GI mates, while I sat on the sofa and wanted to go home … it was not an auspicious event. I spent months saving up to get my shoes mended after that, but had to put it all down to experience. I only had myself to blame, after all. At least I kept my virtue intact – and I'd been on the back of a real motorbike with a real man, finally. Men were always on the prowl with us nurses, and I suppose I just thought men were men, and I guess they thought us nurses were on the make and take, as well, and that we were fair game. I had to keep my wits about me, though, and I did get into some scrapes.

However, I did get sorely tempted one night. I met a wonderful Czech guy, called Joe, who was so handsome he looked like Tony Curtis. He was slick and fascinating, and persuaded me to go 'up town' with him to a party one evening. He was my first proper boyfriend, and I found out he was a male nurse, something that was very rare then, working in a local mental hospital. I really fell for him and we went out a few times; I think I was always a sucker for good looks, and he was really a looker. Anyway, one night we went out to a bar he knew. He told me that he used to be a barman in a particular bar, so he took me to this sleazy dive which was full of American airmen. We went dancing that night at the Locarno in Streatham, and then ended up in Victoria, where he had digs in a shared house. It was the first time I'd ever been back to a man's place, and I'd drunk quite a bit. In the back of my mind I was wondering how on earth I was going to get back to Putney from Victoria, as the last Tube had gone – it was already way past midnight and I was half-panicking about getting back home.

I could tell, however, that Joe was expecting great things from me. We were in his room, kissing, when suddenly he stripped off, babe naked, and hopped into bed. I was frozen to the spot with fear. Of course, I'd seen plenty of male patients naked by then, and was used to dealing with bodies in the raw, but being alone with someone in their bedroom, in a romantic context, and, well, this was totally different. So I sat on the side of the bed, fully dressed, and prim. We had kissed and cuddled, and all that, but now I was suddenly sober. Joe reached out and grabbed me, but I resisted. I wouldn't take my clothes off. It was a mortal sin. I wasn't ready. I wasn't prepared. To my surprise, Joe got very frustrated. 'I've never met anyone like you in my bloody life,' he said, very disgruntled. He stopped being romantic and turned nasty instead. Well, I didn't know what to do. All my life I'd had it drummed into me not to have impure thoughts, or do immodest deeds. I would go to hell. Pure and simple. I remembered the nuns getting me to put my tongue out so they could see the big black stain on it, proving I was a sinner, through and through. I could feel myself standing in the corner at school, and remember the sting of Sister Margaret's pencil on my earlobes, or her large, heavy hand slapping the back of my legs. These strictures were deeply buried in me, and it was hard to leave them behind. I couldn't just jump into bed with Joe, no matter how much I fancied him (which was a lot). I couldn't do that, and I couldn't jump off Big Ben and fly, either.

Joe lay there, his bare back to me, and didn't or wouldn't understand. 'Please, Joe, don't be like that,' I implored. 'It just doesn't feel right – I'm just not that kind of girl.' Joe was implacable, and his back remained firmly turned towards me. I believed in marriage, and also that sex should really be in a loving relationship – well, for me anyway – and I felt Joe was expecting something from me that I really was not in a position to give. If Joe had mentioned marriage, or we'd been engaged, it might have been different. But even then I would have struggled with the morality of it all. This was way before the Pill came in, and way before 'Women's Lib' had hit our female consciousnesses and raised them. I was absolutely paralysed with fear. He lay there, starkers under the sheets, angry with me, and I sat on the edge of the bed, trembling with fear and humiliation. It was a mess. I had no way of getting home, either, and Joe clearly was not going to be a 'gentleman' and help me in any way at all. Amazingly, he just turned his face to the wall and said rudely, 'Go, then.' Just like that. I was horrified. I was heartbroken. I was summarily dismissed. In tears I picked up my handbag and coat, and tiptoed downstairs in this big, old creaky house. I went past the toilet on the landing and was worried that someone might come out and find me creeping about in my state of moral turpitude. Clearly, I was in a state of physical, moral and mortal turmoil. Even being there, in a man's room, after midnight, seemed enough sin somehow to send me straight to hell. I'd been told so many times that God was 'all-seeing' that I surely believed it. He could see me now, as I crept downstairs, my heart in my mouth. I eventually got out onto the street, blubbering with shame and grief. Somehow I stumbled on a bus stop and found a night bus to get me home, where I collapsed into bed just about in time to get up and start the day shift.

Anyway, after that humiliating night, that was it with my beloved Joe. He cut me dead. I was outraged, but I was besotted, so I still wanted him to want me, even though I knew that he'd behaved abysmally. I guess I was very infatuated at the time. I saw him in the Putney Hospital grounds a couple of weeks later, as he worked in a nearby mental hospital, but he just looked the other way – he didn't want to know me at all, which broke my heart. I thought he was gorgeous still (more fool me), and I was very miserable about it, but he didn't want to see me after that awkward night in his room. I was so confused, and of course I knew I should have been angry, and I should have thought he was a cad, but I was simply nuts about him and couldn't get over it. I never told my nurse friends about that night, either, as I felt so naïve. I knew Jenny would have rolled her eyes and said, 'Mary, really, for goodness' sake! Enjoy!' But I knew she'd had some bad experiences and I didn't want to repeat them myself. She and some of my other friends didn't seem to have the same level of conscience that I did, so I just had to suffer in silence about it all. It was just that, for me, sex before marriage was a sin, with a giant, illuminated, capital 'S'.

9

Tragic Love Story

It took me a long time to get over Joe's snubbing of me for not being a loose woman enough. I so wanted to be with him, but I couldn't do what he wanted me to do as it just went entirely against the grain. I was in torment, but, being stubborn, I stuck to my guns. My background went in deep and, as they say, 'You can take the girl out of the convent, but you can't take the convent out of the girl.' I was living proof. The 'S' word, sex, was totally entwined with the 'S' word, sin, as far as I was concerned. My upbringing had drummed into me over and over and over that carnal thoughts were evil, and that I had to control these thoughts – and, of course, actions – at all cost, to save my soul. It wasn't that I was a religious zealot, far from it; it was more that I was utterly terrified of the consequences. Also, what I had seen of the failed abortions in the sluice had chilled me to the bone, and I hated the idea of disposing little bits of babies down the sink, as if they were some simple 'by-products of reproduction' (as they were called). I hated the idea of all that, and I had been deeply shocked by what I had seen on the women's surgical wards. So, despite letting my hair down a little, and the odd kiss and cuddle on Saturday nights after a gin and orange or two, I was chaste, even into my late teens and early twenties. The spectre of my mother and the nuns breathing down my neck and pointing the finger accusingly never left me, and made me especially cautious. I was amazed (and even a little envious) at some of the attitudes of my fellow trainees, like Jenny, and in a way I secretly admired their ability to live in the moment and enjoy life, including all the carnal pleasures, despite the risks. But for me, I was much more wary and kept myself intact, as it were. And experiences, such as with my handsome Czech, Joe, only confirmed how important it was for me to keep myself to myself, despite the heartbreak that it entailed.

I was also incredibly unworldly at this stage of my life. In the early 1950s it was shocking to think of people having sexual intercourse outside of marriage (shocking and also downright dangerous before the Pill came along in the mid-1960s, which gave women more sexual freedom). However, I had never come across anything at all in my life to do with homosexual love, and had no idea that lesbians, gay men or bisexuals existed (they weren't called that openly then, obviously). I guess I had some vague idea about some people, men in particular, being a bit 'peculiar' or 'pervy', or even 'queer', but I had never actually met a homosexual (well, knowingly anyway), and back home we would never have talked about it openly. We might have hinted or whispered if we thought someone was a bit different, but the fear of God was always hovering overhead, and I would never have thought someone was interested in being in love or even having sex with someone of the same sex, as it just would not occur to me. Call me naïve, but that's exactly how I was: an innocent abroad.

Anyway, there was one night in the nurses' home that three of us, Jenny, Hanse and I, had drunk far too much Merrydown, and giggled ourselves into exhausted oblivion. We all fell asleep in my bed, and when the maid woke us up at six thirty the next morning we were all still fully dressed, so there was a mad scramble for those two to get back to their rooms, to get ready for the day. We all thought it was a total laugh and thought nothing further about it. However, Matron got wind of it, somehow (we guessed the maid had gossiped about it), and all three of us were carpeted. I remember standing there, my hands behind my back (yet again), looking down at the carpet, with Hanse on my left and Jenny on my right, like three naughty little schoolgirls all in a row (it was like something out of Gilbert and Sullivan), as Matron told us, in no uncertain terms, that our behaviour was outrageous and unbefitting to our noble profession. 'Three in a bed! What on earth is going on with you?' she snipped. 'Do you not know the hazard of sleeping with women?' I had absolutely no idea what she was talking about. What was the 'hazard of sleeping with women' when it was at home? What on earth did she mean? Of course, I couldn't ask her, or talk back, and Hanse, Jenny and I could hardly contain ourselves, and could barely keep our faces straight, as we mumbled 'Yes, Matron,' and 'No, Matron,' under our breath. When we were released out into the corridor, we padded along to the toilet block, and then collapsed in a total heap of helpless mirth. For months afterwards we would mimic Matron, saying 'the hazard of sleeping with women' as a catchphrase, with absolutely no idea of what she had meant by it. It just sounded so rib-achingly funny.

However, my eyes were soon to be opened in my second year, albeit with tragic consequences. There were two trainee nurses, a lovely Hungarian girl, called Suzan, with shoulder-length dark hair, and an English girl, called Brenda, with a short, brown cut, who were best friends. They did everything together, and were always eating in the canteen, working in the sluice, or folding sheets, with each other; they were inseparable. I took them completely at face value, being me. I had my good friend, Jenny, and also Hanse, and I was used to having sisters at home, with whom I was very close, so it made no odds to me to see women together all the time. I was used to home, the convent and now the hospital. Then one day, Jenny, who was very knowing, whispered to me, 'There's something up with those two, I'm sure there is,' as I watched Suzan and Brenda walking down the corridor, very close, almost hand-in-hand, and chatting animatedly to each other – I really wondered what on earth she meant. 'I'm sure they fancy each other,' Jenny went on. 'What do you mean, they fancy each other?' I couldn't understand what Jenny was getting at. 'What?' 'How?' I'd never heard such a ridiculous idea. 'You know, like *that*,' Jenny hinted, nudging me. 'Just like a man and woman, but they are two girls.' 'Don't be so ridiculous,' I said, and started laughing. 'I've never heard such a stupid thing in all my life. They're just friends – close friends.' 'You mark my words,' said Jenny, not to be put off from pressing her point. 'You just watch them, they are not normal.' So I did.

I began to notice little things: like I heard Brenda say to Suzan one day, 'I've put a nice hot water bottle in your bed,' as they passed in the corridor. I thought, 'That's nice. I'd do that for my sisters,' but I had to admit I noticed a sweet little knowing grin pass between them that looked like more than just friendship. I noticed they always walked along very closely, heads almost touching. When they ate at the table they sat closely side by side. It was like they were joined at the hip. Even so, that didn't prove anything. 'They sleep together, you know,' Jenny whispered in my ear one day, in the canteen. 'What do you mean?' I asked naïvely. 'I sleep with my sisters back home sometimes, especially when it's cold.' 'No, not like *that*,' said Jenny, losing patience with me finally. 'You are silly, Mary. It's not like you and your sisters, it's sex, *you know*?' I didn't know. Not at all. What was she getting at? 'Sex? With women? How?' I couldn't get my head round it at all. How on earth would that work? Sweet Jesus, I thought to myself, I had only just really got to grips with understanding heterosexual love-making, and seeing erect penises, although I hadn't 'done it' myself yet. But homosexual love, now this was a completely different thing. And women? 'But what do they do?' I could see that I was driving Jenny totally mad as she rolled her eyes heavenward, in her usual exasperated fashion. So she leant across the table and started whispering fervently in my ear. My eyes widened, and then nearly popped out, as I had my first graphic lesson in lesbian love-making. 'You've got to be kidding me?' I gasped. 'No, true as I am sitting here,' said Jenny, proudly. I was astounded. Surely women didn't do *that* to each other? And now I looked again carefully at Suzan and Brenda, I could see that they were always linking arms, putting their arms round each other's shoulders, and were looking at each other lovingly and cuddling up, all the time. In a way, it all looked natural, but now I looked at it differently I could see that it was real love, not just friendship. I could now see that they adored each other, and found each other irresistible, just like I had fancied Joe.

I was dumbfounded. I had no idea such things went on at all. Thinking back to Ireland, I supposed now there must have been homosexuals there, but it was so totally taboo and I wouldn't have recognised it, or them, if they had lain across my path, stark naked. It was something I just knew nothing at all about. But now my eyes were opened, I could only see how Suzan and Brenda were all over each other. It was just like the boys and girls on the dance floor on Saturday night, but it was two girls. I couldn't imagine what it was really like to be them. I had never imagined it before. So now, when we all huddled in my room at night, over the Woodbines and Merrydown, the main topic of conversation was the two female lovebirds. We did gossip about them, because we were so curious, and the whole idea was so novel. We giggled as we imagined what they might get up to, and, fuelled by Merrydown, our descriptions got quite graphic and lewd.

It was all good-natured high spirits, largely down to our feeling embarrassed and out of our depth. We didn't send them to Coventry, or anything like that, and tried to treat them just the same way as any other nurses, especially as we had to work together. But I was curious, and I wondered how many other nurses were that way inclined. It made me wonder, too, about all the unmarried sisters – were they closet lesbians, too? Had I missed the clues all this time?

Anyway, things were going to take a turn for the worse, and later on I would feel very guilty indeed about those hours of gossipy drinking sessions we had at the two women's expense. All the gossip must have got back to Matron somehow, and we heard one day that Suzan and Brenda had been carpeted. I guess their behaviour was fairly apparent to all, but I knew it would be pretty serious if they were really two women together in love, and got found out somehow, especially as male homosexuality was still illegal. Apparently, they had been seen separately and told, in no uncertain terms, by an irate Matron that their behaviour had to stop immediately or they would have to leave Putney Hospital. I could imagine Matron being very scolding and cold as she told them they would be thrown out of the nurses' home if they did not clean up their act. We had no idea whether Brenda put up a fight (she was what Jenny called the more 'butch' of the two), or whether

Suzan broke down in tears, but in the next couple of days we could see that they were very unhappy, sitting separately in the canteen or going about their chores on their own. They looked so sad and miserable, not being together, like always, and my heart really went out to them, poor things. I'd been up in front of Matron enough times to know how embarrassing and humiliating it all felt to be told off, and the fact we all knew their business now, as well, I could see that it was totally excruciating for them. Their secret love was out of the bag, and the poor nurse cats were being tortured in public.

Then one morning, soon after the ultimatum meetings with Matron, we heard a loud commotion before breakfast. The maid had knocked on Suzan's door, for her early morning call, and did not get any response. She had hammered and hammered on the door, and then had gone to get Home Sister, who had the master key to her room. They had found Suzan unconscious, and at first they thought she was dead. Suzan was carted off to the women's medical ward, but remained unconscious. They examined her, but no one had any idea what had happened. Had she had a stroke? Or a heart attack? It was all very hush-hush as, back then, something like suicide was not spoken about either. Another taboo. Another sin. Another thing that could not be talked about. Sweet Jesus. However, there was no trace of pills or alcohol, and the doctors were puzzled as to what had happened. She was definitely in a coma, and she did not come round for days. We were all very upset as Suzan was a total sweetie. I began to feel very guilty. Had our gossip got back to Matron somehow? I felt we were culpable in some way and felt dreadfully sorry for her, for them both. Suzan was a quiet, kind soul, who was an excellent nurse, and also was very beautiful. Brenda was beside herself and totally inconsolable. She visited Suzan, and sat by her bedside, in a silent, miserable vigil, but there was hardly any sign of life. Brenda took herself off to her room and we could hear her sobbing at night. It was absolutely terrible. We tried to comfort her, but she locked herself away and wouldn't talk to us. Perhaps she blamed us, who knows.

Then, when they stripped Suzan's bed, finally all was revealed. They found, under her mattress, a syringe and an empty phial. She had stolen a bottle of insulin and had injected herself, and put herself into a terrible coma. The real tragedy was that she never, ever recovered. The insulin turned her into an imbecile, and she was eventually carted off to an institution in Epsom for the mentally ill. She was a vegetable after this, and was only twenty. I guess she might have been in there for the rest of her life. I don't know what happened to her in the long term, but she was just sitting in an armchair, dribbling, and was unable to speak or do anything for herself when I visited.

It was utterly heart-breaking. I felt terribly for her, as it was worse than suicide – it was a living death. Brenda was also destroyed by the whole episode. She had lost her true love, and she could not continue in Putney Hospital, either. So she volunteered to become a missionary in Africa, and disappeared quite quickly soon afterwards. It was the most devastating incident, and we all felt very bad for them both, especially for Suzan, whose life had really ended so badly, so soon. It was such a lesson to me about what happened if you did not fit in, and I felt life was really terrible for lesbians and gay people after that. I vowed that I would understand more, and gossip less – and certainly learn to judge more kindly. We were told by Home Sister not to refer to the incident again, and that we had to forget about it all, and to get on with our lives and our jobs as nurses. The whole thing was never mentioned again, although I never, ever forgot it – not even to this day.

10

Can't Cook, Won't Cook

Despite the deeply tragic love story of Brenda and Suzan, which affected all of us trainee nurses and cast a cloud over our year, life went on in the hospital as usual. At the end of the first and second year we had written exams and a practical, and I was pleased (and a little amazed) to pass them. I had swotted quite hard, as I actually liked exams, and learning (something I'd got from my mother and her quizzes), although I'd been quite naughty at school. I think the practical nature of nursing, of applying my learning, suited me down to the ground. Meanwhile, hospital life was always coming at us, and despite this horrific tragedy we were swept along by emergencies, births, deaths, operations, accidents, duties, chores, you name it. I had learned that it was no use moping, and the hard work extracted out of us was always a brilliant antidote to whenever I felt sad, nostalgic, lonely, worried or angry about something. Working hard was the name of the nursing game, and we were expected to roll up our sleeves and get on with whatever task was thrown at us. Plus, the rigid hospital hierarchies meant that you never, ever questioned what was thrown at you: it was 'Yes, Sister,' or 'No, Matron,' or 'Right away, Staff,' no matter how you felt or what you thought. In that sense, nursing was a bit like being in the military: we were part of a community, part of a regiment, and each of us played our part in 'getting things done'. We had to 'jump to it' and 'turn our hands to anything'. And most importantly of all, we had to be 'at the ready' for 'action' for the greater good of Putney Hospital, and, of course, the patients and community it served. In a way, the hospital was also a microcosm of the bigger society beyond its walls, as it had its own sewing room, dining room, kitchens, gardens and vegetable patches, laundry and mortuary. It was like a self-sufficient medical community, and it was possible for us to live there and never go anywhere else at all (we would have gone nuts, however, if we'd stayed in all the time). Luckily there was a pub, The Spencer, owned by the Spencer family (Princess Diana's ancestors), literally crawling distance across the road from the hospital, so we were able to pop in there occasionally (when we were off duty, and when we had the cash) to get a breather, or to buy our much-needed bottles of Merrydown cider and a packet of Woodbines. Otherwise, life at Putney Hospital was all-consuming, all-demanding, and simply a complete way of living, with its own customs, regulations and quirks.

Although most of our training was on all the different wards – medical, surgical, children's – as well as casualty and theatre during the day, we always had to do a fair amount of night duty, too. And one of the strange things about being on night duty was the fact that we had 'dinner' in the middle of the night. I never really got the hang of it, as my whole bodily system would get turned upside down by the early mornings, late nights, and then the reverse, when I went back to day duty. If I did nights, it was always difficult to sleep in the daytime, and I often felt short of sleep and exhausted. Plus, I missed the daylight, and eating at any time of day or night wreaked havoc with my body clock. But once I was on nights I felt exhausted in the early hours, so having hot food and drink was a very clever way of keeping going (except those of us who crept away and got into laundry baskets or cupboards to snatch a much-needed forty winks). However, it was very difficult to do any of that, as the main Night Sister, the notorious Beetle, was a tyrant and she had her beady eyes on absolutely everyone and her sharp little nose into everything, as she scuttled about the wards.

The late-night dinners were cooked on site in a small upstairs kitchen by a lovely, plump woman called Ivy.

There were no ready meals then, so everything was cooked from fresh, and cooked to order in the hospital. Ivy was a sweet little woman, a proper old-fashioned dinner-lady, who had been in catering for years, and she did all the common fare for the time: sausage and mash, egg and chips, lamb hotpot, chicken pie and mash, liver and bacon or beef stew with dumplings, spotted dick and custard, apple pie and custard, or rhubarb crumble, and the like. All of it very like good old-fashioned school food, which would 'stick your ribs together', and was accompanied usually by a nice cup of tea from a giant steaming urn. There were also scones and buns, biscuits and sandwiches with white bread and cheese and pickle, but we mostly wanted hot food when we were on nights, because we were all starving by two o'clock in the morning. Ivy usually cooked for between ten and twenty staff, and this included the hospital porters, the doctors, the nurses and anyone else who happened to be around on some duty or other. It was a strange late-night world we lived in, but I gradually got used to the routine. I felt Ivy and her hot food was an absolute life-saver for us all; it was nice to chat to other staff, and sit down and rest my weary legs.

So one night I clocked on for duty, and turned up at the men's medical ward, ready for the night's work. Suddenly the Beetle appeared: 'Come with me, Nurse Powell,' she ordered, and set off at high speed. All I could do was say, 'Yes, Sister,' and follow her obediently. She clicked her way along the corridors and then clacked her way up the stairs to the kitchen, with me following behind like a little bemused gosling (although I towered over her really) following a rabid mother goose. I thought, '*What on earth are we doing here?*' and I wondered for a horrible moment if poor old Ivy had had a heart attack or burned herself badly, or something.

Finally, we were at the kitchen door. 'Right, Nurse Powell,' hissed the Beetle. 'You are a junior nurse, and Ivy is off sick, so you are to cook for everyone.' My jaw hit the floor. I must have looked like a bomb had dropped on me, and I started to protest. 'Oh, Sister, no, you see I can't …' The Beetle wasn't having any of it; she put her hand up to stop me speaking. 'Nurse Powell, this is an emergency and you are to cook the dinner tonight. I don't want to hear any excuses,' she snapped. 'An idiot could do this in their sleep, and I'm sure you know how to cook, so go and get on with it, nurse.' And with that the Beetle scuttled away, leaving me open-mouthed and totally panicked. What? Me cook for everyone? This had to be a joke. I had never cooked for more than one or two people in my life, and then it had just been a fried egg and a bit of bacon. I could manage toast – just – and a cup of tea. But prepare food in bulk, from scratch, for a load of hungry, tired and grumpy hospital workers – now that was right out of my league. Absolutely impossible. I had no idea how to do complex stuff, like pastry or puddings, and had no idea about timings or quantities.

I pushed the door and went into the little kitchen, all white tiles and stainless steel, with big pots, pans, skillets and a gas oven. Everything was clean and pristine, and then I looked at the clock – it was about ten o'clock already. Lord, people would start coming in for some food from eleven onwards and I had no idea where to start. '*Oh sweet Jesus*,' I thought. '*What am I to do?*' I honestly can say I panicked. My mouth was dry, my hands were sweating, my knees were knocking – and I wanted to run away. I had never been allowed to cook in my mother's kitchen at home. 'Get away with you, get out from under my feet' is what my mother would cry if I approached the large cast-iron range and stove. 'You'll only go and ruin everything. Get away with you.' My mother had ruled the roost, and she was a good, plain, substantial cook, but we were not allowed to touch. She dominated everything, did everything her way, and liked to eke out what we had, and made sure there was always enough to go round, fairly and squarely. No messing. She kept her five children at arm's length, and out of harm's way, so she was the chief, the chef, the main cook and bottle-washer, and we were her labourers. I learned basic cooking skills, but Mother was boss. And we (well, me, in particular) were simply nuisances. In the way. So I'd never learned to cook for more than a few people. I didn't really have a clue, and I stood glued to the spot considering climbing out the window (except it was the first floor), or disappearing into a cupboard and going to sleep until it was all over. Sweet Jesus, how was I going to get out of this one alive?

Then Percy the porter came in. My prayers were answered, obviously. He was a cheerful Cockney chap in his fifties, in his little brown porter's coat, and he knew me well from all my regular Woodbine orders. I was peering at a piece of paper on the scrubbed wooden side counter where Ivy had written down Friday night's menu (tonight's) as fried fish and chips, peas, apple tart and custard, tea. So it was the typical English fish and chip supper. Yes, I'd had that many times on a Friday night myself, but had never considered for a moment what went into the process of actually creating it. I was already looking at Ivy in a completely different way: Saint Ivy, with a halo the size of a giant doughnut that I loved to eat from the local bakers hovering over her head. 'Nurse Powell?' Percy was standing next to me, looking at me with an extremely concerned expression. 'Are you all right?' 'No, I'm not, Percy,' I said, and burst into floods of helpless tears. 'Whatever is the matter?' Percy was kind. 'What are you doing, girl?' Suddenly, I blubbered all over him, incoherently, stuttering out that I'd never cooked fish in a big frying pan, and I had no idea how to make chips – and for so many people – so where would I start? I'd never used a deep fat fryer, had no idea how long everything took, and I was in a total state. I couldn't do it, I wouldn't do it; and the Beetle would have my guts for garters if I didn't do it. 'What on earth are you talking about?' said Percy, confused. So I explained about the Beetle bringing me upstairs and telling me I had to cook for everyone as Ivy was off sick. I was not able to do the task and I'd be in trouble all over again with Sister – it was a disaster.

Well, Percy, who was usually quite a docile little fella, suddenly hit the roof. He turned into a total Rottweiler before my eyes and sounded really angry, on my behalf. 'Oh, it's not on,' he said. 'You've got to go to the union. That's Ivy's job, it's not your job. You shouldn't be asked to do work that is not yours to do; the hospital ought to have a proper back-up plan – it's a total disgrace.' I blew my nose loudly, just as Jenny came into the kitchen. I took one look at her, my dear friend, and started blubbering all over again. Percy continued, undeterred, 'You've got to go to the union, you have. It's just not on!' Jenny, who was always a bit of a rabble-rouser, joined in with Percy at this point. 'Look, Mary,' she said, trying to get me to pull myself together, 'we are *nurses*, not cooks. You can't cook for everyone, you don't know how. Nor could

I, if I was asked. It's absolutely bloody ridiculous!' I knew she was right, but the thing was an edict from the Beetle. It was simply a matter of 'she who must be obeyed'. An order was an order, and I'd grown up thinking orders were sacrosanct (even though I tried to wriggle out of them all the time). What could I do? 'You've got to go to the union,' piped up Jenny, echoing Percy. And he continued haranguing me, too, trying to persuade me to take action. 'It's no good, girl. You can't cook for this bloomin' lot. You've got no ruddy idea.' I looked up and saw that the dining room was beginning to fill up with people wandering in, looking very hungry and tired, and confused, wondering where on earth their dinner was. Oh, sweet Jesus, it was a nightmare.

So, I pushed past Percy and Jenny, and left them arguing the point, while I looked around the kitchen and examined the contents of an old-fashioned walk-in larder. There were several fish laid out on dishes, covered with greaseproof paper, presumably for that night's meal. What else was there? I found some butter, cheese, and then on the side I found several loaves of white bread, ready for breakfast, I supposed. There were piles of potatoes in nets, but so much time had passed while I'd been dithering and panicking, debating and crying, there was no time now to start preparing anything cooked at all. But still I thought I should try: so I got a heavy frying pan, some lard, and started frying one of the fish. It burnt on one side and started disintegrating, and then I thought, '*Hell, what about the potatoes?*' and started crying all over again. Disgusting fishy smoke was billowing up from the pan. Jenny appeared in my face, turned off the gas, and said, irritatedly, 'It's no good, Mary. Stop it, for goodness' sake. You've got to get the union involved.' 'Look,' I said, 'we've got to give them something. It's too late for all that now – they're all expecting something, aren't they?' I was aware of a queue forming and ravenous staff looking mighty disgruntled and confused, to say the least. 'Will you help me now, if I say I'll go to the union afterwards?' Jenny looked annoyed, but after a moment she thought a bit as she was not one to give up on a fight. But then, to my relief, she said, 'Of course, Mary. Where shall we start?'

Between us we found all the bread and cheese we could muster, and we made piles of thick cheese sandwiches. Everyone was disgusted at there being no hot food available, and there was much shouting and complaining: 'Call this dinner?' or 'Blimey, is that all we get?' We just emptied the larder of all the cold edibles, and hoped for the best. I found a box of biscuits, some slabs of Battenberg cake and some Cox's apples, and there was a general air of disdain, but people were hungry and they fell on what they could get their hands on. Meanwhile, Percy got the urn on, and we made pots and pots of tea, which seemed to calm people down. A good old cuppa, that always seemed to be the thing to smooth things over. I'd learned that was always the English way. Anything could be solved with a nice cup of tea. By the end of the dinner break, which was about three in the morning, I had finally done the washing up and tried to make the kitchen look presentable, at least. I felt like I'd been through a huge experience, and was sure I'd be in trouble with Ivy once she found we'd eaten her week's supply of bread and cheese, and cake and apples.

Anyway, the next day Percy and Jenny went to the union, the National Union of Public Employees, unbeknown to me. Apparently there were clear demarcations about what staff should or shouldn't do, and kitchen work belonged to catering staff, not nurses, and there were strict regulations that covered it all. I didn't realise that things were so regimented by law, and perhaps I was naïve. I thought of Putney Hospital as one great big community and so, in a way, I thought the Beetle had had a right to get me to do something out of the ordinary, because it was a sort of 'everyone muck in' kind of regime. But apparently not. Apparently the gardening staff had different rules to the catering staff, and we nurses were in a different union, or section of a union, to the porters, and so on. This was a total eye-opener to me. I was also surprised, in a way, that people took it all so seriously, although, coming from Ireland, I should have known that anything vaguely political always touched a raw nerve in people and trouble always followed. It always came down to rights, and people getting hot under the collar about wanting to exert or fight for them. I definitely should have known better, given I'd lived with my father long enough, talking about being on the barricades, to know how much it all mattered.

Anyway, inevitably, the next day I was summoned to Matron's office. I was terrified. I knew it must be about the whole night duty dinner incident. Had I cost the hospital hundreds of pounds in using all the wrong stuff? Was I going to be sent home? I was in a real state as I found myself staring, yet again, at Matron's grey plush carpet. That damned carpet, I'd have to bin it one day, ceremoniously, I thought, staring at its bright strips of colour. 'Nurse Powell,' Matron snipped in her cut-glass English voice, 'I believe there was an altercation about the cooking last night?' Sweet Jesus, I wanted the floor to swallow me up – how did she know all this already? I bet it was that bloody Beetle woman. I imagined the letter home to my mother saying I'd been a disgrace to the nursing profession, and that I was thrown out, just as she'd predicted, so I spluttered out: 'Yes, Matron. I can't cook, and I was told to cook, and it was a disaster, as everyone was shouting at me, and I couldn't make hot food, and we had to raid the larder. It was terrible, and I used up all Ivy's supply of food for the week, too.' Matron sat quietly for a moment, obviously thinking. I thought, *'Well, that's it, I'm for it,'* but I tried not to make things worse by saying any more right now. 'Well,' said Matron, slowly, and fixing me with her cold blue eyes, 'I hear Percy has got NUPE involved now. You know it's for the likes of street cleaners, road sweepers and domestic servants, don't you, nurse? Is that what you've come down to?' I couldn't believe my ears. I stared at Matron, unbelieving, and had no idea what to say. She was so icy, such a snob, I'd never heard anything like it in my whole life. But Matron was not finished. 'We're professionals, nurse – and we don't associate ourselves with the likes of NUPE.' I could feel my blood beginning to boil, despite the precarious position I was in. *'"We don't associate with the likes of NUPE" – who did she think she was? The Queen?'* I tried to bite my tongue, but failed. 'But, Matron,' I began to explain, 'Percy's a porter and …' Matron put up her hand, and stopped me, mid-flow. 'Indeed, Nurse Powell, a *porter*, not a *nurse, not one of us*.' 'One of us,' indeed. I felt my face go red. In fact, all Percy had done was try to protect me, and had actually helped me out, got into trouble for it, no doubt. I didn't know what to say. I wanted to melt into an invisible cloud. I stood there feeling miserable: I was always in trouble, always getting it wrong. I could never seem to get it right. Slowly, the tears seeped down my cheeks, no matter how hard I bit my lip.

I'd always been in trouble with the bloody nuns, or my mother, or someone who thought they knew better. Now I was in trouble with Sister and with Matron – and now the union. Nothing would ever change. It seemed everyone around me always thought they knew better, and I always seemed to be the one to mess things up, and end up in the poo. I could hear Matron continuing, so I tried to concentrate and wiped away my tears. 'You've let yourself down, nurse,' she was saying haughtily, 'and you've let the side down.' She paused for effect, and I stood rooted to the spot, wanting this ordeal to end. 'Anyway, you won't have to worry tonight, as Ivy will be back, so you won't have to cook.' And with that, I was dismissed, and had to go back to my duties, feeling less than one inch tall.

That night, hunched on my bed, I described the scene with Matron to an irate Jenny, over a bottle of Merrydown and a packet of Woodbines. However, I was amazed when Jenny even rebuked me: 'Why didn't you tell Matron that she was treating you like a domestic servant, so going to NUPE was bloody appropriate in the circumstances?' Oh, Lord, I was being told off by Jenny now, who was equally disappointed in me. Why couldn't people leave me alone? To do things my way? Thing was, Jenny was always much more feisty than me, and I'd seen her stand up to Sister and stand her ground with Staff. She was used to fighting her corner, and was absolutely great at it. I felt like I always felt at home, squeezed in the middle and utterly useless. Quite often there would be 'murders' in the house, with my mother shouting at my older sisters, with me caught in between; or there would be my mother shouting at everyone, and my father trying to placate her, over my head. Of course, at other times she was a good, caring mother, who taught us to behave, to knit, to sew and to cook. It was often a war zone at home, and now it was a war zone at work, too. And I was still getting it wrong. I felt upset that Jenny wasn't more sympathetic, and I sulked a bit, but we soon found the funny side, as we always did, and after our evening of cider and ciggies, and hot gossip about the rest of the hospital, we put the world and our friendship to rights. In the end, Jenny took me up to London, on a day off, and I joined the Royal College of Nursing as a member. I remember going into this really posh building, and signing up and paying my dues. After a lot of late-night chats with Jenny and my other colleagues, I understood, finally, how important it was to belong to something that did collective bargaining, as individuals always got picked off, somehow. I made sure I read the rule book, and then felt proud of belonging to a wonderful organisation like that, which represented nurses up and down the land. And I would continue to be a proud member of the profession, and the RCN union, which campaigns for us as a professional group as a whole, for the next sixty years and more.

Amazingly, and perhaps fortuitously, I found myself being given a six-week course of 'housekeeping training' soon after the night-duty dinner incident, which included learning how to cook. It was thought that nurses needed to understand a lot about diet and nutrition, and we were taught how to prepare food for the patients with special dietary requirements. In fact, at first, it came down to a lot of scrubbing of potatoes, washing of cabbages and cutting up of carrots. There were big sinks full of vegetables and we seemed to spend hours scrubbing, peeling, chopping, slicing and cutting out all the bad bits for the pig bin. I also seemed to spend hours washing up. I hated this job. The pans were enormous, and heavy, and inevitably had something burned and disgusting on the bottom, so it was scrub, scrub, scrub all over again. I guess it was good training for my later stints in the Lyons Corner Houses, where I would supplement my meagre income with hours of washing up for a few shillings extra. The rest of the housekeeping training involved learning about special diets: for diabetics (no sugar obviously), gastric ulcers (no acidic foods, like citrus fruits) and others. We would spend hours measuring out careful amounts for each particular patient, using old-fashioned Salter weighing scales with brass weights. We would weigh the porridge oats, the cornflakes, the sugar, the bread and milk. It was all carefully worked out, and thus Mr So-and-So on men's medical would get his cornflakes, carefully measured, without sugar, to help him in the morning, as a consequence. We also spent time observing the catering staff as they chopped, sliced, prepared, boiled and cooked, which was great fun and invaluable training for my later life. The very best thing about our housekeeping training was that the day ended at four thirty, after all the washing up was done and stacked up, which seemed like sheer luxury to those of us who were usually running about at the beck and call of Sister and Staff from dawn until dusk. It was almost like going on holiday; at least it was a change, and we learned something that would be useful for ourselves later on in life.

11

Theatre Tales

As part of my training, I had to do a three-month stint in the operating theatre during my second year. I was very excited about this, as it felt like it was proper, serious medicine, and that I would finally be at the heart of the hospital's main proceedings. After all, going down to theatre was always very dramatic, and it was often make-or-break as to whether someone would survive an operation or not. I held surgeons in high esteem, thinking they were absolutely marvellous and I was totally in awe of what they could achieve. I had watched the usually very posh and tall consultant surgeons as they wafted round the surgical wards the day before an operation, and they always looked like demi-gods. The patients would sit up, or lie prone, being very obedient and silent, while the consultant surgeon spoke over their heads to the house doctors and Sister, explaining about the case and what they would be doing the next day. I often felt sorry for the poor patients, lying there, with no idea what exactly was going to happen to them, as they were often terrified of 'going under the knife'. (This was way before it was thought to be a good idea to explain to the patient exactly what was going to happen to them during an operation.)

However, once I'd been in a real theatre, I began to see exactly why they should be terrified. I would have been, too. I'd always imagined that the atmosphere would be a hallowed, silent place, with highly intellectual and medical discussion taking place in lofty tones. Far from it: the theatre resembled more of a butcher's shop, with a lot of chat or loose talk, even jokes, and it was often shockingly brutal in its dealings. Indeed, I learned a lot about how resilient the body really can be from my stint in the theatre, which is where all the real drama of the hospital is played out. At first, I was very frightened of going into theatre itself, as it seemed such an alien, hallowed place. It was a very regimented atmosphere, and even more daunting than the usual routines I'd already experienced under either Sister's or Matron's eagle eyes on the wards. The main operating theatre was a large rectangular room with windows all along the top of the outside wall, letting in light and where we could see the tops of some trees. The room was covered with white swabbable tiles, from floor to ceiling, and the operating table was in the centre under a huge light that could be manipulated to vary its height and angles. There were the ubiquitous sterilisers bubbling away in the trolley room, which was adjacent to the theatre. There were glass cupboards full of instruments and other implements along one wall. It was drummed into me continually that hygiene, sanitation and sterilisation were all of the utmost importance, especially here. It literally meant the difference between life or death, due to the need for infection control. My job as a theatre nurse was, at first, simply to observe. I had found my experience at the morgue hard to handle, but by now, a year into my training, I had seen quite a few things, and lots of blood, pus, wounds, breaks, lacerations, aborted foetuses, smashed spines, and even my fair share of dead bodies. The purpose of any operation was to focus on one precise site on the body, and to do some very fine handiwork, and I was fascinated to watch the procedures that the surgeons seemed to carry out with such amazing deftness and confidence. I would have been terrified to take a scalpel in my trembling hand and cut someone open, but the surgeons seemed to go about it just like they were peeling an orange, and with as little hesitation, emotion or fear. I guess that's why they were paid so much more than us, and also revered by us all – they were the mavericks of medicine.

My job, once I was given one, was to fetch the surgical instruments from the sterilisers and then to lay them out, in precise order, on a metal side trolley, ready for the surgeon to use. The instruments had to come out of the steriliser at the right time, just before the operation: not too early, so that they lost their sterility, and not too late, so they would not be too hot to hold. They had to be put in a certain order, so the assisting nurse could hand them to the surgeon as he called out for what he wanted to use next. The surgeon and his housemen assistants would scrub up in the sluice next door – another room with huge metal sinks and taps – which took quite a time before the operation started. They would scrub and scrub their hands mercilessly with soap and nail brushes. We all had to do that, and then rinse and dry on clean towels. Then they'd put on rubber gloves and the consultant would waft in, followed by his deferential entourage. I remember one surgeon was particularly small, and he had to stand on a box in order to reach his patient on the operating table. This did look fairly comic, although I wouldn't have dared laugh, obviously. It was more than my job was worth. As our hospital was located near to Putney Bridge, we had a stream of young men come in for emergency operations, who had been involved in horrible motorcycle accidents on the Kingston bypass. Back then no one wore a helmet, or very few, and motorcycles were often in collision with lorries, buses or cars. I saw many a lad come in with a leg half-hanging off, or with terrible head injuries, or smashed spine, and these were a real surgical challenge. The poor guys usually lost their legs, if not their lives.

One job I had to do, which always stayed with me, was being what they called the 'dirty nurse' in theatre. I had to put on a big white apron over my theatre kit (a green mask, a hat covering all my hair, overalls and rubber gloves) and stand in the corner of the theatre, by the sink, which was against the wall, near to the sluice. Then I had to catch the limbs and bits and pieces as they were literally chopped out or off. As the consultant amputated some poor patient's limbs, he would wield his silver surgical instruments, which looked like hammers, scissors, even saws and knives, and then he would throw the rest of the leg, arm or other bits of the body that he'd removed towards me. My job was to catch the slippery bloody thing in my apron, and then take it over to the sink and plonk it on the draining board in the sluice. It was really quite gruesome, and I had to pinch myself afterwards quite often that I'd been holding someone's leg or arm in my hands. The rest, like the innards, like spleens and livers, went into silver bowls. It was bizarre and I was often traumatised, I can tell you. I asked one of the less intimidating housemen what happened to the limbs and he said, quite jovially, 'Oh, they'll go in the incinerator.' It was all very matter-of-fact, and there was no room for me to be squeamish at all. What always affected me was the seemingly jolly way in which the surgeons went about their business, whistling, or humming, or chatting about golf. I was very impressed by how confident the surgeons were, but they were definitely a breed apart; dare I say, almost inhuman? I would never have dared to speak to one, and I would watch, fearfully, as they snapped their instructions to the assisting nurse – 'scalpel', 'swab' or 'clamp' – and the sterilised implement would be picked up and slapped firmly in his gloved hand, definitely and surely. I hoped I never had to do this as I imagined I'd drop it on the floor, or miss his hand altogether, as I was so utterly terrified of getting it wrong, and then there'd be an almighty rumpus and more carpeting, no doubt.

In the operating theatre there were a few more things that totally opened my eyes and that I also never forgot (no matter how hard I tried). The hospital had some private patients who would pay for private rooms and treatment, and had usually come through a private doctor, like a Harley Street consultant or clinic. This was despite it being an NHS hospital, in the main. One night I was on call in theatre and was told to scrub up for an emergency operation. I was amazed to see an enormously pregnant

African woman, who I was told was an African chief's daughter, come in. I understood, at first, that we were about to help her give birth. I had seldom seen any Africans, or 'coloureds' as they were called then, so I was quite curious as to how she came to be in Putney Hospital. However, the story turned out to be quite dark, and a real eye-opener for me, as a naïve, Irish girl of little worldly experience.

It turned out she was in the private wing, which was also unusual, as it was usually only very posh, rich white people in there, and the word I heard was that her treatment was being paid for by someone very high up in the British army. I eventually was told, to my horror, that the story was that she had been raped, and the pregnancy was the very unfortunate result. I felt so sorry for her, especially as she was all alone, in a foreign country, facing this treatment. This was obviously before abortions were legal on the NHS (they didn't become so until 1967), so what we were about to do to her, and her unborn baby, was somewhat questionable. It was whispered to me, and I was told not to breathe a word about it – I had to keep it secret, on pain of death. Even so, I was instructed to attend the operation, as I was on duty (I couldn't refuse), and the poor woman was given a Caesarean Section as the baby was nearly at term, but she wasn't in labour. I had never seen a Caesarean before, and I probably hadn't met an African woman either, so I was feeling pretty amazed by what I was witnessing, here in the deep Putney suburbs. However, the most disturbing and shocking part was yet to come, and it would challenge me, in particular, as a good Catholic girl from rural, pious Ireland.

The baby, once delivered, was utterly perfect and gorgeous, and was immediately wrapped in a towel and given to me. I could see a perfect little face, soft eyelashes lying on cheeks, a little button nose and tiny fingers – the baby was utterly adorable. However, I was told to put 'it' on the draining board. The baby was silent, but 'it' was alive. It was definitely breathing as I held 'it' in my arms for a minute or two, wondering if I'd heard correctly. I could feel the warmth of the little bundle, and I could hear it snuffle. Sister told me to place it on the draining board, by the sink, and leave it. I paused for a moment. On the draining board? I asked if I should give her to her mother or hold her myself, but Sister shook her head, and said, 'No, Nurse. Leave "it" there.' I looked at the wrapped-up baby and my heart went out to it – so tiny and helpless, so alone and abandoned, on the large draining board, in a huge, white, soulless room. What on earth was going to happen to it? Was the baby going to be taken somewhere and adopted? Surely someone would take her away from here? But who? I looked around, and was horrified. It was the middle of the night, and the surgeon was carefully stitching up the woman, layer by layer. A Caesarean always leads to a lot of layers of abdomen being cut through, and needing to be carefully sutured afterwards, and this can take some time. I stood, in my apron and mask, eyes focused on the innocent little bundle on the draining board. Surely someone was going to tend the baby? Surely, it could go to someone who wanted one? The baby was alive, for goodness' sake. I looked imploringly at Sister, who looked away and handed more catgut to the consultant with a forced business-like air. It was clear that everyone in the room felt upset about the business: the atmosphere was sombre, and tense, unlike the usual jocular operating-room mood. I eventually left the room, leaving the little bundle uncomforted, unloved and abandoned on the draining board – a tiny white unloved shape in a large clinical expanse. I felt like I had been party to committing the most terrible of all mortal sins – murder. I could not find it in myself to forgive either myself, or the surgeons, for leaving this poor little mite to die. Indeed, I have no idea what actually happened to this particular baby after that, but my worst fear was that 'it' went the way of the amputated limbs in theatre.

Deeply distraught, I whispered to Jenny next day about the terrible baby business, which I felt was deeply shameful and a crime. I felt culpable. She told me it wasn't only the product of rapes or simply unwanted babies that would be treated that way, but also she had seen severely disabled babies left to die, because it was felt that was the best outcome for them. She explained that the product of a white man and an African woman would be deemed a 'half-caste', illegitimate and shameful, so I had to imagine what kind of life it would have all alone on the margins of society. Jenny said they wouldn't really be wanted, or cared for, as they were society's rejects – they would end up in some terrible orphanage in the back of beyond somewhere. But surely, I argued, a living baby is a life, and no one (but God) had the right to snuff them out? Jenny looked at me with soulful eyes, but shrugged her shoulders. Up until then, I had no idea that such practices occurred. I didn't know people thought or acted this way, I really didn't. I found it unbelievable that people would do things like this, particularly people who had pledged to the Hippocratic Oath, which meant saving life, rather than deliberately ending it. I was totally horrified at the inhumanity of it all.

For the first time, I found myself actually wanting to go to see the priest to get this terrible, heavy sin off my chest. Maybe my mother was right after all; maybe England was a 'black, Protestant, Godforsaken country'. It felt pretty Godforsaken after this incident, I can tell you. I felt my faith in what I was doing in England was shaken to the roots for the first time, too. In fact, over the years, since that very dark night in the operating theatre, I have had to confess many times over this particular incident. I did not feel comfortable about not having challenged the practice, and the idea that I walked away and left that poor, defenceless, new-born babe to its fate still brings tears to my eyes, even after all these years. Of course, I felt sorry for that African woman, too; she was just as much losing her beautiful baby, and being used by the ruthless men in the military and the unfeeling system, as the rest of us were colluding with making it happen. It really was a rough old business, and although I got to take things like this more in my stride as I gained more experience, the horror of such things existing in the medicine business and the wider world would never really leave me entirely. The whole incident definitely felt like a dark stain upon my soul.

12

TB Traumas

Again I was lucky to pass my second-year exams (despite my ongoing catastrophes and carpeting), and was rewarded with a different belt, a blue one this time, as I went into my third and final training year. I had to do a six-month placement in a specialist tuberculosis (TB) hospital, called St John's, near Clapham Common. My nurse friends and I were all sent out to different places, so I found myself, on my own, in this new, vast hospital. I felt nervous, as I was used to working with my usual pals, but it was very important experience to gain and we took pride in being able to nurse all kinds of patients in all kinds of ways. It's hard to believe now, but back then, in the early 1950s, TB was rife in the UK, and still largely incurable. It was much feared as a terminal disease and was often spread by spitting in the street and other unhygienic practices. It ranked alongside polio as one of the great killers and maimers, and a major thing to fear (we were used to having iron lungs in which polio patients lay for months, even years, as they could not breathe on their own). TB was a particularly nasty disease, as it actually rotted your lungs, made them become spongy and useless, and led to a long, slow and painful death. It could also destroy your bones and other organs long term. It was truly terrible. In the nineteenth and early twentieth centuries it had been almost a 'romantic' disease as many poets, writers and musicians had faded away on their *chaises longues* due to dying of 'consumption', another word for TB – people like John Keats, Frédéric Chopin, the Brontë sisters and George Orwell. Once you got it, it was usually a death sentence, so we all feared its inexorable rampage through our lives.

In Putney Hospital I had seen plenty of terminal patients by now, and had faced death in general, in the young, the middle-aged and the old, and in men, women and children, but I had a particular dread of TB due to my own family history. Back in Ireland, TB had remained the main killer, too, and was often called the 'White Plague'. Poverty, poor housing, damp, poor diet and overcrowding had meant TB marched on through Irish communities and destroyed whole families, and there was a particular social stigma of being 'inferior' attached to succumbing to it. Sadly, the stringent war years had meant TB was still marching on, largely unchecked, and any signs or symptoms were met with complete horror and despair by all who came across them. So when I started at St John's all my own family experiences came rushing back to haunt me. I would have nightmares. I was already traumatised, and had to handle the trauma of my own memories returning on top of the experience of working in the hospital, which was, in itself, fairly grim.

One of my dearest, older sisters, Una, was always coughing, coughing, coughing during her childhood, or rather our childhood. I could hear her in the living room, or up in our bedroom, going cough, cough, cough, and my mother would be shouting at her, 'Sweet Jesus, Una, will you stop that coughing? You're driving me to distraction. I can't hear myself think with all yer coughing.' Una was a lovely person, so sweet, demure and very pretty, artistic, and I adored her. When she got into her teens I still looked up to her, and felt quite protective of and empathic towards her. Nonetheless, she was still coughing away: cough, cough, cough. My mother continued to be irascible and unsympathetic, so I would feel protective: '*Poor old Una,*' I would think. '*She can't help it,*' when Mother was ranting at her to stop. I suppose I never really thought much about *why* Una was coughing. I just knew she was delicate and poorly, and spent a lot of time in bed, coughing her heart up.

Our mother was fiercely protective of her reputation as a good family-maker and home-keeper, and she made sure we ate well, from all her home-grown vegetables, and dressed well, with all her home-made clothes, so she saw herself as a cut above the average *hoi polloi*. As a consequence, she probably believed that TB was something that only really afflicted the lesser orders, or those who were unclean or starving, and would never have thought that Una could fall prey to such a foul, filthy disease. I guess my mother was suffering from what we would now call denial and snobbery: she just didn't want to countenance what was probably obvious to everyone else who knew or saw poor old Una's struggle with her breathing and health. When Una was coughing, she'd give her some medicine, and say, 'For goodness' sake, stop yer coughing.' The doctor would only be called if Mother thought Una was at death's door – which she almost was, several times – and he'd say, 'She's got growing pains, Agnes. Give her some tonic,' and then charge us seven shillings and sixpence, which was a lot of money in those days.

Anyway, Una's coughing and delicate disposition went on and on, until she was sixteen and I was thirteen. On this particular night Una was in bed, as usual, lying there, reading, sleeping or doing some sewing, and my mother had gone up the road on her own (my father was at Phelan's, as usual) to visit the neighbours to play cards. She would play to win a pound of butter or something like that. I suppose I had got used to Una being poorly; that's just how Una was: permanently sickly, 'pale and interesting', as we used to say. Anyway, I could hear her coughing and coughing, hacking away as usual, while I was downstairs doing my homework at our large, wooden kitchen table. Suddenly, I heard Una cry out 'Mary, Mary,' in a weak, but desperate, voice. She sounded hoarse, but also scared. So I scampered upstairs and found her holding her chamber pot, which usually lurked under the bed, and it was full to the brim with frothy red blood, and there was blood all around her on the pure white linen sheets, the pillows and her pink nightie. I was terrified. I'd never seen anything like it, and I thought all of her insides had come out. And, in a sense they had. I got her a flannel and a bowl of cold water, and wiped her face and hands, and emptied the chamber pot down the toilet, and then got Una to lie down quietly. She looked grey, pale as a ghost, and really seriously ill. I was scared. Was she going to die?

So I ran up the road to Mrs Kennedy's house, whom I knew my mother was visiting, playing bridge, and my mother looked hard at my face and said, 'What on earth's the matter?' I whispered urgently, 'You've got to come now … quick, it's Una …' Once we were outside, I told her about the frothy blood in the chamber pot and my mother's face hardened and she hissed at me, as we walked fast, 'Now you're to keep your mouth shut, and don't tell anybody about her coughing up blood, y'hear. It's worse than having a mental disease.' I was horrified. 'What is it? What's wrong with Una?' I was scared to death. 'It's probably the TB,' my mother whispered aggressively, 'but you're not to talk about it. To anyone. Y'hear? *Not a word to anyone*.' My mother was tearing her hair out because in those days the neighbours would walk to the other side of the street, rather than pass by, if they thought you had the disease. They knew it was incurable, and that it was a definite killer. All this time she'd denied to herself, and to us, it was TB, but now she couldn't keep up the pretence any more.

TB? Not TB? Surely not my dear Una? I was distraught. It was a death sentence, or so I thought, and it was a social stigma: it meant we were inferior, that we lived in dirty surroundings, that we were the lower classes. But we weren't – so it was all very confusing. One thing was clear – my mother was terrified of precisely that kind of stigma, and wanted to keep things secret, too. To me it became obvious – and even more obvious over the months and years to come – that the disease did not pay much attention to class, age or prejudice. If it wanted to get you, it would get you, and often the nicest, kindest, sweetest people would have the worst kinds of disease, like TB, whilst the most horrible, nasty people seemed to survive or get away with the proverbial life of O'Riley. Anyway, the upshot was that Una was whisked away by my father and mother, the very next day, by car to a specialist in Dublin, and was put into an isolation ward in a sanatorium. I think my father must have called in favours and used some of his good friends and contacts to get Una specialist help at short notice – that was the kind of man he was.

At that point, in the early 1950s, there was a belief that TB could be arrested, or contained, if not cured, by putting patients into specialist hospitals for specific treatment. They were made to have a lot of fresh air, so they were often put outside, even in cold weather, in their beds on the balconies. There were also terrible operations, and Una began to have them. Cutting through her back, they took out her entire right lung, which was infected and collapsed, so she only had one lung to breathe with (which was also damaged). It was a terrible operation called thoracoplasty. Along with the lung, they took all her ribs down one side, so her chest sunk in, and her breast disappeared as it had nothing to hold on to. She was very disfigured and badly scarred from the operations and was given a horrible brown prosthesis (it looked like a hairy coconut) for her missing breast which she wore, like a bra. Amazingly, Una went away for six whole years to the Dublin sanatorium: a really long sentence, from age sixteen to twenty-one. When people asked my mother where she was she would tell them Una had gone to stay with Auntie Marie up in Dublin and that she was at college. She was still keeping up the pretence, she was such a huge snob. I heard my mother say to my father, 'Sweet Jesus, if the neighbours find out we'll be destroyed.' The boss of the local health clinic in Clonmell had to be informed, by law, and my father also knew him already, as he'd go shooting with him. He was instrumental in getting my sister into the sanatorium in Dublin, I believe, otherwise she might have died much earlier in Clonmel.

We would drive up 120 miles and visit Una in my father's Morris 10 car. We all went up on her twenty-first birthday, and I had her birthday cake firmly held on my lap the whole way. We were all crying at the sadness of her being locked up in hospital on her day of majority. I missed Una terribly, and she would be thin, pale and very ghostly when we saw her, but she was always trying to make a joke about it all to make us feel better. She was certainly incredibly pleased to see us. As a precaution, Betty, Joan and myself had to have X-rays and tests (which my father paid for), and it was discovered to my mother's horror that the other two also had TB. At this time there was a mass X-ray campaign happening nationally to try to eliminate TB, so we were lucky to have the chance for a diagnosis. Joan and Betty were also sent off to Dublin, to the same sanatorium, for a whole year for treatment. Again, the story was they were with Auntie Marie and going to college. Amazingly, it was discovered that I had had the disease, but that my immune system was so strong that I had actually beaten it off. My brother, PJ, had also recovered. I had scars on my lungs from the infection, but somehow I'd conquered it, so I was very lucky indeed. When we visited the sanatorium, to see all three of my sisters, I hated the place: it always felt cold, huge and scary. Lots of women and men were just lying around on their beds, in candlewick dressing gowns, looking skinny, grey and forlorn. My sisters tried to be jolly, especially Una, but they went through some horrible treatments. Luckily, as we got to the mid-fifties, there were some new antibiotics and other treatments that began to work, and my sisters all managed to survive. Once she was released, she met her husband, and married him, back in Clonmel. Unbelievably, Una went on to have six children.

All this was in my mind as I entered the TB ward for women at St John's. It was a big, long room, with wooden floors, with twenty-five beds running up and down the sides in the usual hospital layout. Along the centre were scrubbed wooden tables, and at the end, near the doors, there was a desk for the nurses and ward sister. The women were all in the advanced stages of TB, and they looked absolutely terrible. They reminded me instantly of poor Una, especially, but also Betty and Joan, although they never got as poorly as Una. These women were all like skeletons, fiercely emaciated, with sunken cheeks and eyes, and were coughing up blood all the time into spitoons by their bedsides. It was a terrible sight to behold, and fearfully depressing, because it was clear, from the start, that these women were going nowhere. The only thing they were moving towards was a long and painful death and the cemetery. I had seen similar people in Dublin, when I visited my sisters, lovely young women who had gradually starved away in front of my eyes, until one day the bed was empty and being stripped down and disinfected. TB was a terrible scourge, and we all felt helpless in the face of it. We spent all of our time mopping, scrubbing, brushing; everything in sight was soaked with carbolic and disinfectant. Every doorknob, tap, wheel, surface, sink, bath, toilet, floor and wall was scrubbed and washed and cleansed, as the watchword was 'hygiene'. We gave the women drugs to alleviate the pain, and would sit and read to them, or play games with them. It was like the Devil's waiting rooms: waiting for them to die. I don't remember any of them going home again. It was as if it was common knowledge that once they entered the ward they would be there until the end, whatever their age, their class, their marital status. I realised then how lucky I had been not only to recover from the disease myself, but also that all my sisters survived, and all went on to have families of their own. As the 1950s progressed, with stronger and better drugs being developed, the BCG programme of immunisation was introduced universally, so that TB was to become, eventually, a disease of the past. Sadly, it has re-emerged of late, but there are drugs now that can cure it, fairly quickly, especially if it's caught early. That would have been nothing short of a holy miracle back in my day.

The third year in the hospital was all about learning about the wider areas of nursing, which we might consider specialising in. I did a bit of maternity and midwifery nursing, which I didn't really take to, and after the TB ward I was asked to visit a local mental health institution. This was an area of social stigma, and one that was feared mightily and seldom spoken about, as mental health institutions were still thought of as 'loony bins' or asylums, and were often depressing, dark, old-fashioned, intimidating places exerting fear over young imaginations. Thus in my third year I also had to visit a local mental hospital as part of my training. It was not something I particularly felt comfortable about, as I had all those prejudices about the unknown and madness, but I was curious, nonetheless. The hospital was in Tooting Bec in South London, and was a big, sprawling, somewhat intimidating Victorian building that gave me the heebie-jeebies just to look at it, quite frankly. However, what I saw there, even on a day visit, really put me off mental health nursing for life. The wards were long and soulless, and with a really scary, heavy atmosphere. I could hear people screeching and groaning, and it sounded a bit like a horror film. The cemetery in Clonmel came to mind, somehow, with the ghouls of the night which I was always terrified of. Sister walked around with a huge silver ring in her hand, with keys hanging off it, as every patient was either locked in their own room, or locked in the day room. It felt like a prison, or a really bleak institution, with a terribly oppressive atmosphere. We were shown the padded cells, which were rooms with walls covered in a thick cream covering, like a sofa, and I could see through the peephole on the door that some patients were writhing on the floor in white straitjackets. These were jackets with arms that could be tied around their backs with tapes, to stop them from either harming themselves or lashing out at the staff. It looked utterly terrifying and barbaric to me.

However, the last straw for me was seeing electroconvulsive therapy or ECT. We had to watch an 'operation' whereby a patient was wheeled into the theatre, then injected with a relaxant, and then electrodes were placed on their temples, and huge amounts of electric current were forced through their brains and bodies. The treatment looked absolutely dreadful, really medieval, like torture, as the patient's body writhed and convulsed on the table, and they bit down hard on a piece of material. The nurses had to hold their bodies down so they didn't bounce off the table or break something. It was so gruesome, I couldn't believe it helped at all. The patients grimaced, convulsed and pulsed. I really couldn't believe that it did any good, although the sister told us that the patients got great benefit from it – largely because it blanked out their memories. But how good was that, really? It seemed utterly barbarous to me, and I hated the whole atmosphere of the place and the ECT procedure in particular. I could see other patients rocking themselves backwards and forwards, with vacant eyes, and others wandering around the wards barefoot, with their gowns open at the back, showing off their bottoms to the world. They were like lost, crazy children. It was a terrible place, and only when I got out of there and back to the relative safety and calm of Putney Hospital did I realise how much my own mood had been affected. I realised on that day visit that mental health nursing was really not for me. I'd be certifiable within a month.

13

Carbolic, Drugs and TLC

After my six-month stint away at St John's on the TB wards and in the mental health hospital I felt very relieved indeed to be back in Putney Hospital: it felt like a real homecoming. It was also great to be back with my nurse pals, and we shared many a gruesome and hilarious story about our respective placements, after hours, hunched on my single bed, over the usual Woodbines and Merrydown. The laughter and the camaraderie were always wonderfully restorative and I realised how much I valued my friends and how much I'd missed them. In my third year I'd become a staff nurse, if I completed my exams successfully. I'd have a different hat to wrestle with making up first thing in the morning (I never really got any better at that), as well as a new royal blue belt with a silver buckle, and a little bow under my chin, all denoting my new status.

In my second year I felt I was definitely making progress in my chosen career. I was beginning to feel some pride in having survived, and succeeded, and actually stuck to my vocation. I knew, obviously, that I still had a long way to go, as there was always so much more to learn. And I wanted to be a really good nurse. However, I felt I had definitely shown my mother I was made of something stronger than she thought I was, and I always had her, and the likes of Sister Margaret, at the back of my mind as I washed out bedpans, cleared up vomit and so on. Sadly, my mother had virtually cut all contact with me, once I went to England, but my two closest sisters, Una and Betty, would write me letters about home, telling me all about the local shenanigans, and I would gobble up the news about my father, my brother, P-J (who had opened a pub, and went on to be the Mayor of Clonmel, twice), and about Clonmel itself. It was always great to hear about our neighbours and old friends, even the church, and sometimes I'd feel very tearful and nostalgic for home. My mother, however, kept a stoical silence as I think she still expected (and hoped) for me to fail. She never visited me in Putney during the first couple of years, or wrote to me to ask how I was doing, or what I was learning. And this did hurt me, deep down – I think it was meant to, of course. She showed her disapproval of my choice of career, country and life by continuing to cut me dead. *'I'll show you,'* I thought, defiantly, as I scrubbed a sink with carbolic. *'Even if I am a bit of klutz sometimes, I'm determined I'll get there. I'll show you that I'll get there in the end.'*

As a trainee, I had seen many things now that had opened my eyes: the six months on the TB ward had been really taxing, and the mental health visit had really unnerved me. The whole six months had tested me emotionally as well as physically, and sometimes the TB wards had all seemed so utterly hopeless and desolate. All I could do for the poor patients was give out pills, check temperatures and pulses, comfort them and try to make them comfortable. And, of course, when they were finally gone and at peace, I would lay out their poor emaciated bodies for their final destination. All the time I had been thanking my lucky stars that Una, Betty and Joan had survived TB and I knew now, deep inside of me, what an utter miracle that had been. I vowed to be as good a nurse as I could be, to relieve suffering wherever at all I could, and to bring to the job all my firm resolve and good humour, as I hated to see people in distress, and with no hope. I realised that nursing was my vocation, my life, and I loved every minute, even when I messed things up. I had been on a huge learning curve since that first day, stepping off the plane at Northolt.

So, being back in Putney Hospital again felt like I was back somewhere hopeful, where I could do something positive and really make a difference. I knew there was more to nursing now than a bar of stinky carbolic or bottles of pongy Dettol, and endless scrubbing; there was an important job of applying as much TLC (tender loving care) as I could, and I vowed to do so at every opportunity. I had seen that there were definitely some nurses, staffs and sisters who became very cold-hearted and hard-bitten: they could be real tough bitches. There was no other word for it, really. I never wanted to be like that, if I could help it at all. Anyway, I was always too soft for my own good, but I thought I'd rather be a softie than be a tough old boot, who didn't care a toss about patient welfare or quality of life. The patient came first – and that was my personal motto. And it has stayed with me, for my entire nursing life, which has spanned over 62 years, all told, in the NHS.

After my finals I would have to do a further probationary year in order to complete my training. This was compulsory. We had to stay on at Putney, and it was like a consolidation year. Only at the end of this were we allowed to be called SRNs, and wear our special belts and badges, denoting our professional status. I had come this far and I really wanted to complete the process. During my third year there were times, however, on the women's wards, when I felt sorely stretched and when I felt I needed to challenge authority (which didn't go down very well with the higher-ups). This was difficult to do, but after seeing the treatment of the poor African woman and her baby something had changed inside of me – I had definitely lost some of my wide-eyed innocence. I had also gained more confidence as I went on through my training.

There was one woman in her forties, called Marjorie Green, who had final-stage ovarian cancer. She was in a corner bed, near Sister's desk, and she was in terrible pain. The only treatment was morphine, which was administered every four hours. When patients were very sick, or nearing death, they were positioned near to the nurses' desk, so they could be visited frequently and monitored easily. Marjorie was in absolute agony, and would start wailing and groaning: 'Is it time yet? Can I have another injection, nurse? Pleeeeeese.' It would only be a couple of hours since her last injection, and morphine was not allowed to be given in less than four hours. But I would think, '*The poor woman is dying. What does it matter? Surely it can't hurt to give her any more, at this stage? Why can't we relieve her pain, for goodness' sake?*' I was appalled that she was left in so much agony. I thought, '*We would put a dog or cat down if they were in that level of pain, then why not a human being?*' I went to Sister and asked if we could give her anything to help her. Sister looked at me coolly and said, 'Nurse, you know full well it's not four hours yet.' 'But, Sister, she's in terrible pain. Can't we give her anything at all?' Sister just brushed me off coolly with, 'You know the rules – just get on with it, nurse. You have plenty to do.' I felt like hitting her, and once in the lavatory I had a good cry. I couldn't bear to see such suffering. So I would go and sit next to her and hold her hand, and mop her brow with a cool cloth, or talk to her to try and distract her, or moisten her lips with some water on cotton wool. I wanted to comfort her in her suffering, poor thing. Sadly, I was eventually washing down Marjorie Green's body, and laying her out, and thinking how terrible her last days had been, with so little respite, as she only lasted a couple more excruciating weeks after that. I cried the whole time, as I prepared her poor emaciated body, thinking how wrong it was that we could not relieve her pain any more effectively. I thought it was an awful way to go. It felt so terribly sad, especially as she was so young and attractive. I really thought, as I washed her thin limbs, that the medical profession could surely come up with something better to help people have less agonising ends to their lives. It seemed so undignified somehow. Pain and death seemed to diminish everyone; it took no prisoners. Luckily, during my lifetime in the NHS, changes have now happened, as modern drugs and new procedures give proper pain relief until the end. However, it was all fairly barbaric back in the early 1950s, and watching someone suffering a long, slow, painful death was a real life lesson for me. It made me even more determined to look on the bright side and to help people wherever I could – even if I was a bit clumsy about it sometimes.

When I had time on the children's ward, it got even more challenging emotionally at times. The children's ward was downstairs, and was a large, airy room with wooden floors and white walls, with a frieze of nursery rhymes round the top, with about fifteen beds. It had large bay windows at one end that looked out over the Common, and the mobile children would get up and peer out wistfully at the other children playing on the grass, or watch others free to play ball with their friends or families. I'd feel sorry for them, particularly because my own childhood had had so much wonderful freedom in it to roam around our large, leafy garden, in the fresh air with the apple and plum trees. I had been out playing all day, pushing my little pram, scrumping apples, collecting pop bottles, larking about, climbing trees, getting muddy, and then I'd look at these poor little mites, all bored, sick, lonely and sad, and see many of them only had a visit from a mum, dad or gran for an hour a day, if they were lucky. A lot didn't even have visitors as travel to the hospital wasn't that easy, and not many people had cars back then. Otherwise the poor children were seen and not heard in bed with absolutely nothing to do. In those days children had to be tucked flat in and quiet ('Arms under the blankets, please'), and they might do a puzzle or read a book, but there was no TV, no radio, no internet or video games – nothing like that at all – and the rest of the time they were simply bored or suffering, lying there. So I would sit and read to them or tell them stories and sing little Irish songs and ditties to them, or simply amuse them by pulling silly faces. I'd do anything to raise a smile, basically.

I got particularly fond of a lovely little girl, Megan, with red ringlets, who was only three. She was such a sweetie, and she was so small and delicate that she was still in a cot. She had cancer, poor thing. She had a little ball of cotton wool that she would play with and talk to. I got her a little teddy and she would cuddle it to herself for comfort while I told her stories. When she was in pain, she would lie very quiet, and stare at the ceiling. I found it dreadful to watch her in so much agony. Or she would cry and groan incessantly, and it was a terrible sight to behold. When little Megan died, she was not even four yet. I remember picking up the little ball of cotton wool that had been her constant companion, and holding it to me, and not being able to stop crying myself. I could hear my father's voice in my head saying, '*There she goes again.*

Her bladder's in her bloody eyeballs, crying over everything,' but I felt crying over a dying child was actually appropriate. I did seem far softer than most of my friends, however, who seemed to take suffering, death and dying more in their stride.

Of course, there were also back-breaking, yet poignant, moments that went along with certain aspects of the job. On the women's ward we had all these poor old girls with broken bones hung up on huge metal tractions which were constructed round their beds like scaffolding. They had broken hips and broken femurs, or fractured legs all swathed in heavy white plaster casts. Or there'd be broken pelvises hung up in slings, like the stork brought the newborn babies in. Some would have screws through their knees or hips, linked to straps and contraptions, keeping everything in place. Back then patients were kept fairly immobile for long periods as the risks of thrombosis was not really understood like it is today. So patients with fractures were strung up on traction, which was like metal scaffolding, and could be in hospital for weeks, even months. If they were on traction, say with a broken femur, we had to give them bedpans by heaving them up and on to them; it usually took two nurses, one each side, to do that. There were basic handle hoists then for patients to pull themselves up on, but it was the nurses' backs that took the strain, and many went off with quite serious back injuries, pains and strains as a consequence. Quite often the bedpans would spill over, so we had to change all the sheets under them, with the patients still attached to their traction, and then bed-bath them all over again, so it was quite a palaver. You had to watch the older ones as they would often not tell you that their bed was wet, because they felt too embarrassed about it, or they might be so far gone that they did not even know themselves. They were also at risk of suffering from bedsores, also known as 'pressure sores'. These were not simple things that we could ignore; bedsores could become infected, and if they went deep, over time they could actually kill a patient. So we had to make sure that the immobilised patients were treated properly, and every time they were on the bedpan, and had their bottom washed, or they had their daily blanket bath, we also had to treat them with surgical spirit, so that it would harden the skin on their bums. We also put surgical spirit on their elbows, heels and shoulders for the same reason. It took time and effort to do this for every patient, but it was preventative medicine, proper nursing care, as we knew they needed to stay well. All this had to be fitted into our busy day, and was seen to be an essential part of the job. Caring for the patient, making them comfortable, preventing sores and keeping them clean and hydrated, even putting flowers in a vase when relatives visited, was a real act of daily TLC. We didn't just leave them in bed to fester; they had to be turned, or moved, or talked with to keep their spirits up, and their beds always had to look spotless and clean, ready for Sister's or Matron's twice-daily, spit-spot inspections.

There was something else that happened that challenged my thinking in the second year of nursing. A rumour starting going around about one particular night sister, a very unfriendly and rather brisk woman in her forties who we called 'the Grim'. She always seemed very snappy and had no time for idiots, especially me. She looked awful a lot of the time, thin and pale, quite yellow-looking, and most of us nurses hated her. If the Grim was on nights, I knew better than to get in her way, as she would always be snapping at me, '*Stop dawdling, Powell. Get on with it*,' or '*Haven't you finished folding that linen yet?*' She was the kind of woman who was never satisfied, and along with the Beetle she was one of the night sisters we were always trying to dodge. She was notorious for making you do a job again and again and again, and I sometimes felt she was a right sadist, never satisfied, almost inhuman, like a machine. Rumour had it that she had had her heart broken during the Second World War, and that her beloved had not returned to her. Her life and all her future plans ruined, plus all prospects of motherhood and family life gone, she had thrown herself full tilt into her nursing career, but we sensed that, underneath it all, she was terribly hurt, bitter and sad. She was never kind to the nurses, and quite harsh with the patients, too, and sometimes I really wondered why she was a nurse at all.

Anyway, one night a huge scandal broke in the kitchen while I was on nights having dinner with my good friend and confidante Jenny, who was always the fount of all knowledge and gossip. Jenny, who was a year ahead of me, had now passed her finals, thankfully, and was in her probationary year. I always looked up to Jenny, as she was braver and more feisty than I was, and being a year ahead she could warn me, and teach me, in equal measure. Like a veritable bloodhound, Jenny had her nose to the ground, as always, and as we finished our spotted dick and custard at one in the morning she whispered to me she had the most amazing story to tell me. I had noticed the Grim had been absent the past couple of night duties, and I just assumed that she was ill. 'You'll never believe it, Mary,' Jenny hissed, her eyes like saucers. 'The Grim's been suspended!' 'What?' I leaned across our dirty bowls. 'Sshhh! Mary, shush.' So I leaned nearer. 'Come on, spill, Jenny – what on earth's going on?'

It seemed that the Grim had got overly fond of helping herself to the contents of the locked drug cupboard while on nights (only the sisters and staffs had keys). When drugs were dished out to patients every four hours we usually took them round each bed on a special trolley, which had a key which opened it up, like a little bureau. The drugs were loaded up from the charts, and given to each patient to take. Back then things were more gung-ho than they are now, and the drugs would be dished out in a little bowl or popped in a glass, and then left by the bedside. It seems that the Grim was working all sorts of shifts, back to back, working day and night, in the NHS and local private hospitals, and that she had been keeping herself going on amphetamines. She was popping Dexedrines like sweets, and had apparently been caught trying to sell them to other nurses and even doctors. Apparently, a trap had been set for her and she had fallen for it. Dexedrine, or 'Dex' as it was known back then, was very popular, and apparently used a lot by people on shift and night duties. It seems that military personnel and police would take them, as well as medical staff – it was illegal, of course, but it was well known as a way of keeping awake on long night duties. People also took pethidine, which was a kind of morphine, and was very addictive. So the Grim was a drug addict. Apparently, too, the Beetle had helped set the trap. Sweet Jesus, what next? I was astounded. When I looked back, I realised that she always seemed so nervy, so full of irritation and snappiness, that it all began to make sense. She also always looked terrible, like she could do with sleeping for a week and eating a good, wholesome dinner or two. I also heard that she had been doing shifts in the local Lyons Corner House as well, doing washing up, which many of us did, to make ends meet. I didn't know why she needed so much money, but maybe she was overworking to blot out her bereavement – who knew? She must have been caught in a terrible cycle of addiction which had started around the time of her boyfriend's death. We never saw her again, thank goodness, so never really got to the bottom of it all. She just disappeared under a cloud of shame. I think the hospital quietly dismissed her, and, like many things, it was never spoken of again and was brushed under Matron's grey carpet. What did surprise me, though, was to find out how many of my colleagues had been popping pills to keep awake – including the doctors – and I found myself realising, yet again, what a naïve and trusting person I was. It really was time for me to wise up.

* * *

There were a couple of things that could have put me off nursing for good: one was all the frothy blood that was on the TB ward; the other was vomit, of which there was also copious amounts. I wasn't so bad with poo or wee, but I always hated vomit, and it was one of those things that could make me retch myself. Anyway, one night I was on the men's ward, and one of the patients woke up and called out, 'Nurse, nurse, come quick. I feel sick.' He was an old working-class boy in his sixties, a Mr Peabody, and so off I went and fetched a white kidney-shaped bowl from the sluice and pulled the curtains round, as he threw up everywhere. It took a while to clean him up, which involved changing his sheets and pyjamas in the middle of the night. However, he was soon settled down again, so I took his vomit bowl to the sluice and threw the contents down the drain. I scrubbed and washed myself up and was just going down the ward, back to my desk with its little light, when I heard 'Nurse' again, coming from Mr Peabody's bed. 'Oh, Lord,' I thought, 'not again.' So I went over to Mr Peabody's bed, where he was now sitting up looking quite agitated. 'What on earth's the matter?' I asked, thinking the poor man must be about the throw up again and I'd have to rush off to get another bowl. 'It's me teef, nurse,' mumbled Mr Peabody through his gums. 'Where's me teef, luv?' 'What do you mean?' I was getting irritated now, but I had a horrible feeling I knew what he was getting at. 'I'd 'em in,' he said, simply, 'when I wus sick.' *'Oh sweet Jesus, no,'* I thought. *'They're probably down the bloody sluice.'* I didn't let on, but I tried to buy some time. 'Wait a minute. I'll go and have a look for you,' I said, innocently. So back I trotted to the sluice, and I had to literally put my hand down the yukky drain. Although we had rubber gloves on, everything went right over the top of my cuffs as my arms dug deep into the sluice to fish through the vomit, the poo and whatever else was in there. It was utterly and completely revolting. Anyway, it was eventually worth it, as there was Mr Peabody's teeth, his pink and white NHS gnashers, rolling around in the bottom, on the verge of disappearing down the drain. I managed to rescue them, and I washed them off, scrubbed and disinfected them, and scrubbed my hands, as well. Then I popped his dentures into a beaker with a sterilising tablet and took them back to his bed. Mr Peabody was pleased as Punch. 'Oh, you are kind, luv,' he said, ever so grateful, through his gums. 'Fank you, nurse.' He had no idea what I had had to trail my fingers through to get them, but he didn't know any better, and he was happy as a little lamb as a consequence, so I was very pleased to help.

* * *

Although I was usually kind to the patients, there were times when my own patience was running short. With men like Mr Peabody I always felt I had a bit more slack, as they were nice old blokes, who had very little in life, were stoical and seldom complained about anything. They ate the cold, tasteless hospital food, they accepted the hours of boredom and the poor pain relief, and were always up for a joke or two. Like Mr Poysner and his Sunday whelks, I never minded getting them a paper, or helping them with their baccy, or making them comfortable in some way, as hospital was pretty boring, and the days were long and fairly lonely for them. However, there were times when I had some old dears that really drove me mad. I also think that as I got older and more experienced I felt I could stand my ground a little better, especially with so-called 'difficult' patients. There was one old girl, a Mrs Mason, on the women's medical ward who used to irritate me; it wasn't her fault, she was about 80 and she was always demanding something, calling out, trying to get out of bed at night, and generally being a nuisance. Looking back, she was probably heading for dementia, but we didn't know much about that then; she was just 'old' and 'senile'. I think I was more tolerant of this when I first started, but by the end of my second year I was beginning to see I had to have firmer boundaries with some patients – otherwise I'd be run ragged all night. This one particular night, when I was on duty, Mrs Mason knocked her water glass and jug off her bedside table in the middle of the night. Sometimes the old dears had nightmares, sometimes they had bladder infections or the heebie-jeebies about something or other, and I would go and sort them out. They would be moaning and groaning in their sleep, or shouting out like banshees. It wasn't their fault, but it meant I had to get up from the desk and go and wake them up, and then settle them down again. Anyway, this night, in the middle of winter, I was cold and I had been sitting at the desk with my cloak on. We often did this if we were freezing and struggling to stay awake, especially in the early hours after our dinner break (which was always the worst time). I had a big black torch, which I would use to shine on the patient to see what they needed and to help them out. Otherwise the ward was in complete darkness, as we knew the patients needed it to be pretty dark to get to sleep. When I got to Mrs Mason's bedside she was pulling everything off her side cupboard, and taking off her clothes, throwing things about and trying to make a big old mess. I could see that she was going to wake everyone up, so I snapped at her, 'Now stop it. Stop pulling everything around, and settle back down.' I was quite sharp with her, uncharacteristically so for me, but I felt there would be pandemonium on the ward if I didn't watch it. Anyway, she said, 'Oh, dear!' and sounded really shocked, and stopped what she was doing immediately. I then helped her on with her nightie, and settled her back down, tucked her in and tidied her up. I said, 'Now go to sleep,' in quite brusque tones. *'Sweet Jesus, I think I'm turning into the Beetle,'* I thought briefly, but I'd really had enough and I was tired.

Anyway, all went quiet after that, and I thought to myself, 'Oh, goody, she's gone back to sleep. Thank Goodness for that. Now we'll get some peace.' Next morning, at five, we always had to wake everyone up for their early morning temperature and pulse readings. It was always an irony that we had to disturb them only to have to get them back to sleep again. Anyway, as I got to Mrs Mason's bedside and woke her up, she suddenly clung on to me with her bony hand. 'Oh, nurse,' she said. 'I've had a terrible night.' She proceeded to tell me then that she'd had a dreadful nightmare, and that a big black bat had come to her bedside with a big light, and had threatened her. 'I think it was that bleedin' bitch of a sister,' she said. 'You know, that little rotten one that comes round at night.' Well, I knew who she must be thinking of, the Beetle, whom all of us thought was a 'bloody bitch' (I'd done a pretty good impression, obviously). I wanted to put her straight, but I found myself unable to say anything, as I thought I might end up in fits of giggles and give the game away. 'Oh dear,' I said. 'Perhaps you should complain?' 'Oh, no,' Mrs Mason said, really scared now. 'If I complain, she'll only come and get me again. I'm so scared of her, nurse.' 'Oh, I see,' I said, all innocence. 'Well, would you like me to tell her off for you?' 'Oh, would you, nurse?' she said, her eyes widening and beginning to tear up. Well, I did feel terrible then, as I was leading her a merry dance. 'I'm scared she'll come back and do it again,' she said. I had clearly shaken her to her roots, and I felt a bit bad for her then. 'No, don't you worry,' I said innocently, patting her hand. 'I'm sure she won't come round and scare you again. But you have to behave yourself, you know, and be a good girl, get some sleep at night and not throw your things about.' 'Oh, yes, nurse,' Mrs Mason said meekly, clearly having learned her lesson. 'I'll do anything not to have that big black bat scaring me again.' I have to say we did laugh about this over our fags and booze debrief later, although I did feel sorry for the old dear, as I had clearly given her a real fright. She was as good as gold afterwards, and I began to realise that nurses could exert quite a lot of power on the wards, if they really wanted to. Luckily I didn't let it go to my head, especially as I didn't want to end up like a bloody Beetle or a Grim.

* * *

At other times we had good fun with the patients. When it was the Grand National we would create a sweepstake and patients would put a shilling on to win and would be arguing the odds over a copy of *Sporting Life*. It was heart-warming, and I would see all these old geezers with heart conditions or terminal cancer having a laugh and debating about who was going to win or get placed. We were happy to see them feeling happy, as it made the job easier if patients were not feeling miserable and down. And at Christmas we really went to town. We nurses would spend ages decorating the wards: we'd make paper chains and hang them up, bring in a little Christmas tree and decorate it, and string up loads of lovely Christmas decorations. Then we would rehearse and not only perform a Christmas pantomime, like *Cinderella*, but also sing carols, and we'd go round each ward giving an individual performance. It was an amazing production always, and we did it with gusto. It reminded me of putting on our plays and operettas back home, so I didn't mind singing, dancing, acting and generally making a fool of myself. I could also help make the costumes, too. A lot of us were on duty over Christmas, and also had no homes to go to ourselves, so the kitchen would produce a proper Christmas lunch on Christmas Day, and a surgeon would always be delighted to come in specially to carve the turkey, with great precision, for each ward. They'd come in and we'd all stand round watching them sharpen their knives to do the honours for their patients, as the hospital was a kind of family, too. We all had crackers and hats, and we'd sing carols with everyone. The Salvation Army (we called it the 'Sally Army') would often come round the wards and play to the patients on their big brass instruments, and there would be a festive, if restrained, atmosphere. Those patients who were well enough would be sent home for the holiday, but there was always a hard core of patients left, including children, who were very sick or even dying. One of the doctors would dress up as Father Christmas and dish out presents from a big mail sack which had been donated and wrapped by Friends of the Hospital. It is not an exaggeration to say that it felt like a proper community, a big, happy family even, and we got a lot of satisfaction from making the patients feel that bit better. Making this kind of effort was part of the job and we felt it was important to make some kind of home-from-home for people who had no other choice than be in hospital over the festive season. It was fairly miserable being in hospital, otherwise. So this seemed especially important because visiting hours were only for an hour a day, and were very strict, so the children, in particular, felt very lonely, especially at Christmas or Easter. It does sound a bit goody-goody now, but I think I learned a big lesson at Putney Hospital about the importance of emotional happiness and contact with patients, and giving regular TLC, as being an essential part of helping patients to get well physically, or even to face the worst outcome, the end of their lives.

14

Private Rooms and Community Life

It's very important to remember that the NHS was only four years old in England when I started my training, so it was a relatively fledgling national institution, still finding its way. Putney Hospital had been built with private money in 1908, and although it had been taken over by the NHS in 1948, private money was still needed to fund all sorts of things. All NHS hospitals in the United Kingdom had boards of governors and patrons, who constantly raised money for new equipment, or specialist instruments, or to build new hospital wings or rebuild old wards. So since its inception the public health life of the hospital had had to live alongside private health (and wealth). I didn't pay much attention to all of this, but I knew there were a few private patients tucked away in private rooms. I knew that in Ireland we had had to pay for our medicine, and often people went without health care simply because they were poor. I also knew this was changing rapidly now the NHS was in place, and thank goodness for that. We had been lucky with my sisters and their TB treatment as my family was relatively well off and my father was well connected and used his good friends and contacts to our advantage. So when I was at Putney Hospital I gradually became aware that not only did most wards have one or two side rooms that were reserved for private patients, who paid, but there was also an actual private wing tucked away in the hospital with nine paying beds. The same nurses tended to both the public and private patients, and they largely ate the same food as the NHS patients, and had largely the same standard of accommodation. The only real difference was that the patients could come straight into hospital either by being referred by their GP directly, or by going straight to a consultant, who would put them at the top of their list. As ever in life, money talked.

When I was a junior nurse (that meant during my first and second years) I remember being sent into the private wing to clean. That was the only level at which I was allowed to enter this hallowed territory. I remembered being sent in with a cloth and a canister of Vim, which was a tough scouring powder, and I was told to make everything shine. I had to polish the sinks, the brass taps and bung holes, the plug chains, everything within sight, until they shone like new. This was all done with my bare hands, so the skin was almost peeling off after I'd scoured every sink, toilet, bath and nook and cranny. I was told to keep my head down, and not to speak to anyone and not be nosy (almost impossible for me, of course). On Sundays, when the cleaner was off duty (or when she was sick), I also had to mop the floor with those big, wide floor mops, which was exhausting, if good muscle-training. Thus, as trainee nurses we were not unleashed on the private patients to nurse them until our second year. I don't think it was felt we were good enough, or even sophisticated or savvy enough, to know how to treat them. After all, they were obviously a better class of person than we lesser beings, as they had money; and, of course, there were often famous people or well-known public figures on the private wards, and it was probably felt that a more mature, more experienced nurse would be the most appropriate kind of woman to unleash on these noble creatures.

I found out that there was quite a dark side to the private wing. It was often the place that the abortions were done in, as they were paid for privately – and these affected women of all ages, and all classes and backgrounds (like the poor African woman I had attended in theatre, and whose termination had apparently been paid for by the high-ups in the army). However, it was only those who could get enough money together who were able to pay for going private, obviously. It was all hushed up and no one spoke about it, really. The other poor women, with usually failed abortions, ended up in women's surgical and had to mix in with everyone else, and the nurses and sisters could be very punitive and disapproving indeed. The benefit of going private for someone in this unfortunate circumstance was that they were able to get seen to quickly, and relatively anonymously. Plus, being alone in a room gave them privacy and a place to grieve, with some respect. I certainly noticed that the consultant surgeons who were performing these operations, and even the anaesthetists, drove to Putney Hospital in swanky cars, such as Rolls-Royces and Mercedes. These cars were not easily paid for on an NHS salary, I was sure, so it showed that performing private abortions could be quite a profitable business, especially before reliable contraception, like the Pill, was available generally for women. I only knew a little bit about this all going on, but I was sure that my mother would have been outraged – it was exactly the kind of thing that would make her spit teeth and call England a 'Godforsaken black Protestant country'. However, I also learned that there was an even darker side to the private wing that I had not anticipated at all.

Although abortions were not really spoken about, we all knew they happened: it was a sad old business, but a tough part of life. However, there was also a practice that, again, my mother and the nuns would have fulminated against if they had known it was happening, and especially if they had known I was in any way party to it at all.

I was doing a week's stint on the private ward during my third year, and it was summer. We had the windows open, and it was warm and sunny during the day, and still quite warm and pleasant at night. When I arrived there was a very elegant woman, a Miss Pringle, who was a buyer for Harrods, in a single room. She was forty-five, with a curly perm and a handsome face, and had pancreatic cancer, which was a terrible disease to get. She was in the terminal stages, and was in an awful lot of pain. I found her incredibly polite and genteel, and it was so sad to see her looking sallow and yellow, fading away, all on her own, so I would chat to her. She was a nice, educated woman, who would tell me about her job – she was unmarried and didn't have children, obviously – and how much she loved buying furniture for the store. She was worldly and knowledgeable, but extremely lonely as she declined. She didn't have many visitors and I felt so sad that she was facing a painful death without having someone to hold her hand. I would arrange her flowers, and take her temperature, and she would want to talk a little bit, and I would listen, and then she'd have her morphine injection and fall asleep. However, the morphine would wear off, as it always did, and she would be in terrible, agonising pain for a couple of hours between the injections. It was awful to see her suffer so.

The difference in attitude of the higher-up staff on the private wards compared with the ordinary wards was fascinating to see. I noticed the sisters were much more attentive and polite, and the doctors came round more frequently and stayed longer at the bedside. I also saw that Sister or Staff would call the doctors if there was a query about something, even quite trivial, and get them to pop in on the ward, much more than they would have done on the public wards. I guess I learned the lesson that money really did buy you better health care, and that you simply got more attention if you could pay for it. And yet, the patients were still just human beings, like everyone else. The only difference between them and the people on the other wards was the fact that they had a bit of lolly tucked away or were wealthy by family or had earned well. Anyway, one evening, a couple of weeks after the buyer had been brought in, I was on night duty again on the private ward. There were nine beds in this ward and only about six were filled that night. Miss Pringle was still there, and was still slowly deteriorating and in pain. I popped in to see her, said 'hallo' and tidied her bed. She looked dreadfully shrivelled and vulnerable in her bed, and her face looked quite yellow and sallow. Sister came up to me at 11 o'clock and told me to go to dinner, and to take my time coming back. 'Have a nice leisurely dinner, nurse,' she said to me, pointedly. I looked at her questioningly. I can honestly say that Sister had never, ever said anything like that before. Usually it was 'Get back as soon as you can – don't hang about, nurse,' or 'Eat your dinner, but don't take for ever about it, you haven't got all day.' But this night Sister was looking at me a bit strangely, and saying things like: 'Take your time, nurse.' I had a weird feeling that something was up, but had absolutely no idea what it was at all.

All the way through dinner I felt spooked and uneasy. I usually wolfed my food down, and it often didn't touch the sides. But tonight I ate slowly, chewed my food and took the full hour, which seemed incredibly long for some reason. I read a magazine, and then went back to the ward, wondering what was really up. When I got there I had a shock. Miss Pringle was dead. She hadn't been near death when I left, although she had been in pain. I knew the signs of oncoming death by now, as I had seen it many times, and although she was perhaps a few more days, even a week, away, it wasn't imminent as far as I could see, and certainly they hadn't been there when I went for dinner. When I went into the sluice I found two doctors silently washing their hands. That was strange, as usually there was just one doctor on the rounds. They looked round at me, over their shoulders, warily, and there was something in their glance that let me know I had to leave the room and say nothing. Similarly, Sister was acting strangely. She told me quietly to lay out Miss Pringle, but she didn't look me in the eye. The silence hung between us, and as I went to get the bowl of water and equipment to prepare her I felt a deep sense of unease. I knew that something had happened, but I wasn't at all sure what. Had she had a heart attack? Or a stroke? If, so, why wasn't Sister talking about it as she usually would? As I washed her down I felt terrible, and the tears pricked my eyes as always. My Catholic upbringing made me feel like I had colluded in something terrible, and I prayed for Miss Pringle's soul, and also the souls of the doctors and Sister, as I washed the still warm body in the eerie silence of the middle of the night.

Next day, back at the nurses' home, I had a late-night conversation with Jenny, my fount of all knowledge, about what might have gone on. We were half hanging out the windows in my room, as it was a hot summer night, and passing the Merrydown bottle between us. Jenny listened to my story attentively and then explained what she thought had happened. 'Look, Mary, you wouldn't know this, but it's actually quite common practice for two doctors to give a lethal injection simultaneously, with a syringe in one arm each, if a patient wants to end their life.' What? I'd never heard of such a thing. 'You mean it's a kind of suicide?' 'In a way, yes, but she's got the doctors to do it for her, instead of doing it herself. It's called euthanasia, or mercy killing,' explained Jenny. 'It's a way of ending your life, but because it's an illegal practice they get two doctors to do it at the same time, so no one doctor can actually be prosecuted.' Jenny told me she had seen something like it herself before on the private ward when she had been on nights. 'But it's a criminal offence!' I was outraged. I believed in the doctors, and I also believed in the Hippocratic Oath, and I suppose I had drunk in all my life that it was a cardinal sin to take life. Only God had the right to take life away. Surely it was murder, by any other name?

Jenny explained further that patients who had the money could simply pay for this kind of treatment. It was done on the quiet, and it wasn't supposed to happen, but it was something that had gone on for years, apparently. I was really and truly shocked. And yet, when I thought about it, I remembered Miss Pringle being in such terrible pain, and not being able to deal with the lack of morphine relief. What would I do in the same circumstances if I had the means to pay for it? It had been drummed into me to suffer naturally, and to accept death, but what would I do if I had the means to end things another way? She clearly wasn't worrying about the state of her soul, and maybe you wouldn't care about that if you were in such terrible agony. How would I know what I would do in similar circumstances? I suppose I remembered all the lessons about the saints and how they suffered and how it purified their souls. But I had seen many patients die slow and painful deaths, for what reason? Surely, it didn't purify their souls to suffer so badly; surely it just crucified their spirits? I began to notice that many of my colleagues also whispered about cases of euthanasia, and the fact they went on, somewhere in the hospital. It hadn't registered with me before, but now I had actually witnessed it happening (or rather, witnessed the before and after of it) I felt it must actually be true. However, I always felt like it was a terrible dark secret, as if I had committed the crime myself, by not stopping it, and not reporting it afterwards. I used to live in fear of it being found out, and over the years the demise of Miss Pringle ate away at me. It was difficult for me to let go of something like that, as it brought up terrible conflict about what was right and wrong in the situation. I always struggled to do the right thing, so when I colluded with the wrong thing I didn't like myself for it. I wished I'd had the courage of my convictions to go and tell someone about the practice. But who? I presumed now that the high-ups knew all about this practice, and condoned it. But then I also wished that pain relief was better, so patients didn't have to suffer. After all, you wouldn't let an animal suffer like this in similar circumstances. It did take the gloss off the doctors for me, though, when I saw their Rolls-Royces and Bentleys, and thought, '*Ah well, money can buy you death, an abortion, anything apparently illegal, and those who commit the crime can come out well, too.*' The scales of innocence had definitely fallen finally from my eyes.

On a much lighter note, our private wing was sometimes graced by the presence of Hollywood actors or famous people. It was often like royalty was coming. Again, junior nurses would be sent in, ahead of time, to scrub and brush, skivvy and rub, until everything sparkled and gleamed. And then one winter's day I was on duty, and came onto the private ward to find the actor Jack Hawkins, who lived in nearby Richmond-on-Thames and who had fallen in the snow and had broken his shoulder. All the nurses adored Jack Hawkins, who had recently been the star of a hit film called *The Cruel Sea*; he was the bee's knees at the time, the George Clooney of his day. He was a real star, very manly, with a deep gravelly voice, and hunky good looks and a tan. We all fought over plumping up his pillows or changing his sheets, and there was a fight over getting his bedpan, even. He had some famous visitors, such as the actor Richard Attenborough and his wife, who lived in Richmond, too, and we were all literally hiding in the wings, wanting to get a glimpse of them. They were like gods to us. We didn't get their autographs, but we did ogle them from afar.

Apart from stars, we also got some very high-up business people. I remember we had a director from the posh shop Liberty's in central London (which I'd never even been into), who had stayed for a couple of weeks for an operation. He was a delightful man, and we liked him a lot so we did as much as we could to keep him happy. It was always insisted upon that we treat the private patients well, so their drinking water was changed regularly, and their pillows plumped up and sheets straightened, and we made sure we responded promptly when they rang their buzzers. We went and got them newspapers and fruit, even alcohol and cigarettes, when they wanted it. When the director left he gave each of us a £20 voucher for the shop, which was a huge amount of money, probably equivalent to hundreds now. I remember Sister telling us that we were not allowed to keep this money or any gifts at all. We all said 'Yes, Sister,' and looked meek, but then we were naughty nurses and kept the vouchers anyway. We needed the money, and I was not going to pass up £20 worth of goods; indeed, none of us could afford to do that.

What did Sister think we would really do? It was another thing for my conscience to wrestle with, but when I finally went to Liberty's and bought myself some wonderful material that I got made up into a suit, I was really very glad that, on this occasion, I had defied authority and broken the rules. I didn't think it was the worst thing in the world, and to be frank I was absolutely delighted with the result; I had the suit for years and wore it until it dropped off me, finally, in shreds.

At that time there were pockets of poverty all over the south-west of London, and Putney had some pretty rough areas tucked in behind the more salubrious parts. There were old-fashioned Victorian tenement buildings that had no heating, lots of damp and outside lavatories. There were also overcrowded flats and a lot of deprivation, despite the more leafy and red-brick suburban areas around the hospital itself, which I was used to by then. As part of my training I was sent out on my rounds with a bag of basic bandages and medicines, to attend to people in their homes, like a District Nurse. I loved meeting people and talking to them, and I found it fascinating to visit them, and see how they lived their lives. It certainly changed my view that all English people were rich and posh, as I learned that poverty and deprivation could happen anywhere. In particular, I liked working with the elderly. I always had time for them, and I think they reminded me of the kinds of people I had sat with as a child, like the old lady back home, with her Parkinson's. When we visited the elderly locally, we would make sandwiches and take them flasks of hot soup or cocoa that had been made up in the hospital kitchens. A lot of the work was basic, giving them a wash, cleaning them up, bandaging their wounds or sores. Quite a few of the local elderly were living in quite squalid, cold and damp conditions, and I could see they had little to eat. They would sit in a chair all day, and if they were lucky they would sit hunched over a few bits of glowing coal or a single-bar electric fire. But this could be too expensive, so they were often bundled under blankets and eiderdowns, trying to keep body and soul together.

One awful, smelly flat I went into had a granny sitting in her high-backed wing chair. The place was filthy, unheated and really stank of wee, and I felt it was very unsanitary indeed. There were four young children in the flat, with a baby crawling around on a fairly dirty lino floor. The granny was trying to keep an eye on the baby, but it was the smaller children who looked after the babies. The children's mum was out somewhere, and there was a huge Alsatian in the garden, chained to the fence. I noticed the granny's hands were very swollen and red; it looked like chilblains or something like that. I asked the eldest child, who was probably about eight or nine, what her name was and she said 'Monday'. She told me the other kids were also named after the days of the week. When I asked her why her granny's hands were so red, she said, 'That's where Mum keeps hitting her when she tries to get out of her chair.' I was horrified. Each time Granny tried to move, Mum would hit her, and she'd pee herself in fear. Then I saw there were black marks on her neck and breasts, and she was being hit all the time. 'Mum pushes her in her chair with her walking stick,' volunteered the child. 'Every time she gets up, she gets pushed back down.' I was outraged and had to tell the authorities what was going on when I got back to the hospital. It was terrible. I found out that the old lady got moved to a local nursing home eventually and had a lovely four years after that of relative peace and happiness. I visited her once she was in there, and she grabbed my hand and said, 'Thank you, dear. I'm in heaven here.' It really moved me to tears and it made me wonder just why people did such things to their own flesh and blood. She turned out to be quite a lively old lady, and she loved mixing with people. So instead of sitting in her chair all day, being bullied, she was experiencing some level of relaxation, freedom and well-being in her final years. Her daughter was had up for assault and battery, plus neglect, I am pleased to say.

However, her poor children were taken into care and were eventually fostered, and I felt bad about that for a long time afterwards. Every time I had to make this kind of intervention, I always found it heart-rending, but what else could I do? It wasn't right, and something had to be done about it, so I had to do something. Else I couldn't live with my good old conscience, Catholic or not.

Another time, I was walking down the street in Putney and I passed a local rough pub. There were a load of men drinking in there, it must have been early evening and I was on my way back to the hospital. I heard, 'That's the fuckin' bitch that got my kid taken away,' from a man's voice behind me, and then I felt a thump on my back. Instinctively, I turned round and landed him one back on his shoulder. I didn't recognise him, but I guess he was related in some way to the woman whose mum had ended up in the nursing home. I didn't mean to, but it was a natural thing to do, to hit him back; it was self-defence, I suppose, and I felt provoked. I thought, '*Sweet Jesus, bloody cheek.*' It didn't hurt him and he was drunk as, by the time I came to my senses, I saw that his friend was dragging him back into the pub, saying, 'Just forget her, mate.' He was definitely the worse for wear, and I just carried on, hoping that I wouldn't get reported at all. I didn't want another carpeting in front of Matron, with her saying, 'And what exactly did you mean by thumping a member of the public, Nurse Powell? You know we have our reputation as nurses to keep up. What were you thinking?' Or worse, would I get arrested, myself? How would I explain an incident like that to Matron, or even my mother? Thing was, I often didn't think, I was often very instinctual, and I would react to people and situations before I thought things through. This meant I was often compassionate and caring, but it also meant I often got into trouble, or overstepped the mark, because I felt passionately about something and couldn't leave it alone. I certainly enjoyed my times of going out into the community, but it was a totally shocking eye-opener, and taught me where my real nursing interests lay – I did love working with the elderly, and it was something I would come back to, later in life. It would also give me great experience for dealing with all manner of people, in all sorts of situations, for the rest of my working days as a nurse and medical practitioner.

15

Kidnapped

To relieve all the tension and stress from endless training, studying and also long days of fulfilling duties and obeying rules, my pals and I still loved going out, as often as we could, to let our hair down and go dancing. There were still a lot of GIs around at that time, and I remember being whisked round the dance-floor quite a few times by a particularly ardent, good-looking Yank called Hank. He was very keen on me, but I kept my distance, as always, and although I enjoyed dancing, and the drinks, and the laughter and fun, and even the odd kiss and cuddle, I always wanted to get home intact (as it were), and sometimes that was a bit of struggle, I can tell you. A lot of my nurse friends were 'going steady' by the third year, or were actually engaged, and a couple had left, impatient to be married and settled down. I didn't think I wanted to marry, particularly, at least not yet. I felt I had time enough for all that, as first I wanted to live, to work and enjoy some untrammelled freedom. My friends and I still used to go up Putney High Street on our days off and window shop, look at the fashions, get our hair done, or go to Zeta's and drink coffee or have afternoon tea, and we were all beginning to think about what would happen once we got through our final exams, which were looming large at this time. I was pretty scared of the exams, and failing, so I knew I had to make a real effort to get through. I couldn't fall at the last hurdle, so I knew I'd have to buckle down and concentrate. I was desperate to do well. I also knew that I would have to do a further year at Putney, a probationary year, from 1955 to 1956, and only then would I be properly qualified as an SRN. The fourth year was an essential part of the training, and, as I really loved my job, and I really loved learning, I didn't want to mess it all up by getting over-involved with a man too soon. I'd seen enough nurses go off with fellas, like Wendy had, and jack it all in, and, frankly, it did seem a shame. But they were happy, and who was I to judge? Indeed I did feel, sometimes, that it would be nice to have a steady boyfriend, to have someone special who cared about me, who was fun to be with and who made me feel like a million dollars. I did look a bit enviously at my friends who landed nice guys, or were sporting their engagement rings (although they never would have worn them on the wards or on duty – strictly forbidden), and I did wonder if there would ever be a 'Mr Right' out there for me, somewhere, some day, somehow.

We used to go to the Castle Ballroom in Richmond, where there were two large dance halls. One Saturday night I was going up a grand staircase just as a tall, dark-haired man was coming down, holding a pint of beer. I passed him, and instead of grabbing the bannister I grabbed his beer mug, and of course beer went flying everywhere. Oh, sweet Jesus. Typical Mary, so clumsy, and I wasn't even tipsy, so no excuse. Oh Lord, he was awash and I was embarrassed. There was a lot of mopping up to do, but he actually laughed about it, although the beer was all over his trousers, and my skirt was sopping too. We went off to the bar and mopped ourselves up, and got another drink, and he bought me a Dubonnet and lemon, and we soon got chatting. I found him very attractive, a real good-looking charmer, and I soon fell under his spell. This was Brian Mann. He was English and a salesman, and I liked him at once. We got onto the dance floor, and he was soon whizzing me round and I felt absolutely wonderful in his arms. After this first, inauspicious meeting, which ended with a kiss, we started going out. He literally swept me off my feet, and I felt Brian was dashing, intelligent and fun, worldly and also very magnetic. We really 'clicked', and it was the first time I had wanted to spend time with a man. He soon became my official 'boyfriend' and then, amazingly, he asked me to marry him fairly soon after we met. I thought it was a bit too rushed, but I was flattered. He seemed to be the sort of man who made his mind up, and pursued what he wanted single-mindedly, and I liked that about him. He was romantic and adamant, and I was drawn by his energy and enthusiasm. However, I told him I'd have to think about it, but pretty soon I was sure that he was 'the one'. I was twenty and probably felt that after my probationary year we would marry, and set up home together – although after all the struggle I had had to do my training I didn't really want to give up nursing, just like that, which I knew I would have to do, if I married. Women had to stop working once they got hitched in those days, and I knew that would be an enormous wrench for me. I loved my work and I liked my independence. So, I felt there was no real rush, although it was lovely to finally be sharing my life with a man, planning a future and, who knew, maybe even have children and a family of my own at some point. Brian probably felt the need to marry quickly more than I did because I was still circumspect about keeping my virginity, and I felt I had to be married first. However, he was loving and kind, and I thought I had really met the right man for me.

However, there was one fly in the ointment. In fact, not a little fly, but a very big fly indeed. In fact a huge, flying black bug: my mother. Brian was an Englishman. He was also not Catholic and had no interest in converting (not that I would have asked him, anyway). I couldn't imagine what I was going to do, or how on earth I was going to tell her, and the rest of my family, that I was going to probably marry an Englishman and also live in England – all the things that were the very worst possible sins that I could commit. I knew my mother would take it all very hard, and that I would probably never be forgiven. I was already living the blackened life as it was, and now this news would send her completely over the top. I had had so little contact with her all the time I was training that, in a way, it shouldn't have mattered. But it did. She was my mother, after all. I had been indoctrinated from birth to take her opinion seriously (even though I largely defied it), and I knew it was going to be a hell of a difficult task to break the news to her about what her silly, wayward daughter was going to get up to next. Sweet Jesus, I put it off and put it off. And then I put it off some more. Brian, meanwhile, was getting more anxious about setting a date, so I felt I had to do something. I eventually wrote to my dear sister, Betty, confiding in her that I had a boyfriend and I thought I was madly in love. Betty, being a sweet and kind person, was all for it. She told Una, and they both had a breadth and depth about them, possibly because of their own sufferings with TB, that meant they both thought I should grab what happiness I could, whenever it presented itself. Betty had lost a year or two of her youth, and Una had spent a long six years sitting in a sanatorium, where the doctors and nurses were wonderful, but hidden away from all the fun and all the noise of life, to think about things. Thus, I always found that my two sisters were a wonderful sounding board, a great support and allies. Una wrote to me encouragingly, '*Mary, just enjoy your life, as it can all be taken away so easily. Brian sounds like a lovely man, so I wish you all the very best. Just take good care of yourself.*' She told me Betty was right behind me, too. Of course, I would blub over these kinds of letters from Una, because she was so kind and caring, but I still had no idea how I was going to break the news to my mother, or even my beloved father, who also hated the English with a passion. I'd have to cross that rocky old bridge when I came to it.

One morning in the autumn of 1955 I was on the men's medical ward taking a patient's temperature and blood pressure when Sister arrived at the bottom of the bed and stared at me. 'Matron wants you in her office immediately,' she snapped coldly. I thought, '*Oh Lordy, what on earth have I gone and done now?*' I racked my brains as I was tucking the man in, wondering if my late-night scamperings in through the bottom window in the nurses' home had been rumbled, or maybe I'd given the wrong drug to the wrong patient, in my rather loved-up state. 'Oh, and change your apron, nurse,' said Sister frostily. 'It's a disgrace.' I looked down and it was a bit messy, so I rushed to the laundry room, changed my apron, washed my hands and brushed my hair, and arrived at Matron's office ten minutes later. I stood on her doorstep, my heart in my mouth. How many times had I been here over the years at Putney? I should have been used to it by now, but I never knew how I was going to come out of these carpetings, and my pulse was racing, as I simply couldn't think what it was at all that I might have done wrong. Had I forgotten to empty bedpans in the sluice or even set my room on fire with Woodbines? I usually knew when I was in for it, as I had an inkling of what misdemeanour I had committed, but today I had absolutely no idea. So I screwed up my courage and knocked on the door. 'Come in' ushered icily from within, and I opened the door, walked in and nearly fainted when I saw who was beside Matron at her desk.

There was my mother and my brother, P-J, standing bolt upright, almost to attention, staring right at me as I entered Matron's office. My mother was wearing her best Musquash coat (only brought out for very grand occasions), and her hat with the pheasant feather, and my brother was in full naval uniform (he had joined the navy, as an engineer, a couple of years earlier), and it crossed my mind he really looked quite idiotic standing there in all his official kit. My knees went weak and I thought I was going to collapse and thought, '*Jesus Christ, what on earth are they doing here?*' Matron could see I was shocked, and gestured my mother and brother towards chairs, but they refused to sit down. The only thing I could mumble out, stupidly, was 'Who's dead?' and immediately I thought my father must have had a heart attack or that Una had gone back into hospital, and had died, or that Betty was sick again. Matron looked at me meaningfully, and she said, 'Your mother had said she put you in my care, in my charge, and that I've let you get away with murder.' My mother was now eyeballing Matron, with an air of haughty fury, so I looked at P-J, who was looking at the floor, embarrassed. I couldn't understand at all what was going on. I was dumbstruck. I had no idea what on earth she was talking about. Matron looked at me, with ice almost forming on the inside of her little steel-rimmed glasses. 'I believe you have a boyfriend. Is that so?' Oh no, so that was it: my mother had got wind of Brian. And then I knew what this was all about and my knees weakened. As my mind was racing, I then remembered writing to Una the excited letter about Brian proposing to me, and how I'd said yes, and how much I loved him and all that jazz. I had tuned out Matron, and realised I was missing all that she was saying to me. '… and so your mother has told me that you are going home with her at once.' 'Whaaaaat?' I half-shouted, then stood there, open-mouthed, on the damned carpet, yet again. 'But surely …' Matron put her hand up and stopped me. 'I'm sorry, Nurse Powell, but your mother insists that this is the only possible course of action, *in the circumstances*.' 'What circumstances?' I was trying to think fast, to stem my total confusion. Then I began panicking, almost hyperventilating, and the tears started, as always. 'But what about my exams? They're this year. I have to finish …' I stammered out. And at that, my mother finally spoke directly to me, for the first time in years. 'Ah, well, you should have thought about that before you got yourself involved with a Godforsaken Protestant Englishman, now shouldn't you?'

Then I found myself being summarily frogmarched to my room in the nurses' home, stood over, berated and barked at while I packed, while I was crying helplessly all the time. Then I was frogmarched to a bus stop, and thence to the airport, then frogmarched back to Dublin, and finally on to Clonmel. I was in my mother's iron-fisted grasp. It all seemed to be happening in a dream, and I couldn't believe it was happening to me. It was like a nightmare, but I couldn't wake up. I couldn't believe my mother had actually got herself onto an aeroplane and travelled overseas to England and actually found Putney

Hospital. I also couldn't believe that she had the gall to remove me from everything that was dear to me. I was in a state of complete and utter shock. I could see that P-J was embarrassed by the whole thing. I refused to speak to my mother the whole way home, but cried the entire journey. I had had to leave Putney without saying goodbye to my dear friends Jenny, Hanse, Christe and Susan – even thinking of Percy and Bert the porters, or Ivy the cook, or Lily the seamstress, and especially Sister Tutor, my major ally, made me cry helplessly. I even felt some strange fondness for Matron and the Beetle, which showed how far gone I was. I kept asking P-J, 'What on earth has gone on? Why is she doing this? How can she take me like this? I don't understand.' One problem for me, that P-J pointed out, was that I was still under twenty-one, and thus a minor in legal terms, so my mother was pulling parental rank. It seemed that Una had let slip at supper one evening that I had found a beau, and my mother had gone absolutely ballistic. She had interrogated Una and Betty and finally wrested the letters out of them both, and read them for herself. My mother was beside herself and had decided that I had gone completely over to the enemy. I had to be taught a lesson, obviously. So I had to be brought back immediately, shown the error of my ways and brought forcibly to my senses. P-J told me she was completely implacable. Even my father had tried to reason with her, as had my sister Una (who felt terribly guilty) and Betty, whereas my other sister, Joan, had tended to side more with my mother. P-J said he felt sorry for me, but had been dragooned into 'rescuing' me as my father staunchly refused to step on English soil, even to accompany my mother on her moral crusade. It was unbelievable. Worse, I had had to leave without telling Brian, and I was due to see him the very next day. He would have no idea at all where I had gone, or why. There was no way of letting him know. It was all a terrible, awful mess. It was my life, my vocation, my love, my world, and now it was all totally ruined. I was a lost cause.

Then it all got a lot worse. If it possibly could. My mother had got it into her head that I was mentally ill. She dragged our family doctor round and I was put under the medical microscope, like an insect on trial. 'Doctor,' she barked, in front of me, although I was crying uncontrollably, 'I have had to get Mary back from that Godforsaken place she insisted on working in, and where she's gone completely off the rails, just as I predicted. I truly believe she's been studying too hard, and it's all got on top of her. I believe she has mental problems. Just look at the state of her.' Indeed, I could not stop crying, I was incoherent, and the doctor, seeing my obvious distress and confusion, prescribed Oblivon, a very strong tranquilliser. My mother stood over me and made me take the tablets. 'I knew going overseas would do you no good, you wayward girl – but you wouldn't listen' was all she said once I was confined to my room. I slept for almost an entire week, and every time I woke up my mother was there, giving me soup or tea, and making me take more tablets. She literally had me locked in – I was a prisoner in my own home, and my mother the prison guard. My mother would stand over me and tell me she didn't want the priest to find out I was going to marry a bloody Protestant, and an English one, to boot. But I was in love, I tried to explain, and I was going to be married, through my miserable tears. 'Well, that's the problem, isn't it,' she hissed venomously. 'Over my dead body.' *'Don't tempt me,'* was all I could think, but the drugs made me so woozy, and I felt so defeated, that all I could do was fall back on the pillow and sink down further into dreamless, drug-laden sleep.

I was locked in by my mother for three months. I literally couldn't go out of the house – the door was locked, and I was under house arrest. My sisters were still at home, and they stood guard, too. My only ally was Una, who was sickly still, very delicate, and was terribly sorry about having given the game away. I got so depressed that, despite the tablets, I just cried and cried every day. I was back to square one, back to where I'd started at seventeen, and there was no escape. I'd say to my mother, 'Why isn't he writing to me?' And she'd say, 'See, you're soon forgotten.' I was kidnapped, a prisoner. I was missing my friends, missing Brian, even missing the sisters and the porters; I was missing my whole way of life that I'd established – and the freedom, of course – over the past two and a half years. My father was implacable, too. He was under pain of death to agree with my mother and, anyway, he had always hated England and the English, so he wasn't a natural ally. The tablets also made everything seem far away, unreal and woolly, so I would sit like a zombie or do a bit of knitting or needlework, but I couldn't really be bothered to finish anything. I had no idea how on earth I was going to get my life back on track. My mother kept getting repeat prescriptions from the doctor, and maintaining to one and all that I was having some kind of breakdown. Well, I was – but it had been induced by my mother kidnapping me! My brother P-J had scuttled back to his ship, so I was abandoned and I had absolutely no idea how I was going to get out of this situation and back to my life. I was also sad that I hadn't had any letters from Brian, or indeed any of my friends all this time, although I had written letters, and asked Una to smuggle them out of the house for me. It was a terrible situation and I was trapped.

Anyway, one morning I was lolling around in bed feeling sorry for myself, when the front doorbell rang. My father went to open the door, and there, on the doorstep, to his astonishment, was Brian Mann. I was in my bedroom and snuck out on the landing, alongside Una and Betty, and was utterly amazed. My father was blunt and to the point. 'Who are you?' he said (although it must have been pretty obvious, thinking about it). 'I've come to see Mary,' said Brian, unabashed. It was lovely to hear his voice: he sounded so warm and friendly – and very English. But my mother flew at him, on the doorstep, like a maternal Rottweiler from hell. 'Get off my doorstep, you bloody Protestant bastard,' she was screaming. Meanwhile, I was crying and shouting, 'Brian, Brian,' down the stairs, like the lunatic I'd actually become. Una and Betty were hysterical by now, too. Brian was shouting over my parents' heads, 'Mary, I've come all the way from England to see you. What on earth is going on? Where have you been all this time?' My father suddenly leapt into action. 'Hold the door, Agnes,' he said, in a fury. 'I'll get the shotgun.' Una started screaming now as my father was going to the gun cupboard to get his hunting cartridges and loading his gun. Sweet Jesus, he was going to kill another Englishman in front of our eyes. As he was doing this, Brian was shouting over my mother's head, 'Didn't you get my letters, Mary? Why didn't you write?' I was shouting back down the stairs, 'But I wrote to you, Brian. Why didn't you write?' By now my father was back at the door, aiming his gun straight at Brian, right between the eyes, with Una and Betty screaming over the bannisters, 'Don't shoot him, Daddy, don't shoot!' I was sitting at the top of the stairs, crying and screaming, 'Brian, Brian.' My mother turned round and screamed at me, 'Get back in your bed. See what you've done.' My brother had recently married a woman called Esther, who was staying with us, and I could also see her hanging over the bannisters, next to Una, with her eyes like saucers: she must have been wondering what on earth it was she had married into. Meanwhile, Brian was still standing on the doorstep, with my father aiming right between his eyes. Brian was shouting, 'I'm not going. No, I'm not. I'll go when she tells me to,' he said pointedly, meaning me. So I crept downstairs in my pyjamas, tears streaming down my face, and cried, 'Brian, go back to England. Go away. I never want to see you again.' It wasn't true, but I didn't want him dead on the doorstep on my behalf. I knew my father had killed an Englishman before, and I believed he would have done it if things had gone on any longer. So that was it, and off Brian went. As he turned and walked away, my heart broke into a thousand pieces, watching him go.

* * *

After this incident, I was incensed. Incandescent was more like it. I was still drugged and spending most days in bed, but I wanted to know about the letters. So I got Una to find out for me what had happened. She managed to uncover the plot, by asking around, and discovered that my beloved father had got Sean at the Post Office to intercept the letters to me from England, and the ones from Brian had been burned by my father, in our grate at home. Literally thrown on the fire. I couldn't believe he would do that to me. It was an offence, but actually, worse than that, I was amazed that my father would do that to me. It shook me to my roots. I guessed my mother must have persuaded him to enact this insane plan. I also wondered what other letters he had destroyed 'for your own good, Mary'. I was utterly miserable. I wrote to Sister Tutor and smuggled the letter out, via dear old Betty, saying I wanted to go back to Putney as soon as possible and was missing everything. I just hoped the letter got to her. Then one day Betty came in and sat with me, stroked my hair and said, 'Oh Mary, you're so unhappy, aren't you?' I blubbed and said, 'I am. I've got to go back, somehow. He'll meet somebody else, and I'll lose him. I'll lose everything I've worked for. I can't bear it.'

Then a letter did actually arrive at the house from Putney Hospital. It was addressed to my parents, and, for some strange reason I will never understand, the letter was read and not destroyed. It was from Sister Tutor saying that I was a good nurse, a great trainee, and that if I came back immediately I could sit my finals. I had missed nearly four months now, and it was January 1955. In the letter Sister Tutor explained that there had been a huge train crash in December in Barnes, which had been a major disaster. I hadn't even heard about it, although that wasn't surprising as I was under house arrest. I was shocked to hear that a train had not braked, had crashed at speed into the station and fifty-five people had died. The injuries had been terrible, and Putney Hospital, which was the nearest medical centre, had been completely overwhelmed. Sister Tutor wrote to my mother: '*It was an absolutely terrible disaster, and we had bodies all over the corridor. We needed all hands available and we realised how much we missed a hard worker, like Mary. We need her to come back immediately, we need people, like Mary, who are dedicated nurses.*' Reading her letter, Betty kindly decided to help me then. She gave me the fare to get back to England, which was a lot of money then, and helped me escape. She said, 'You go. I'll tell them when you've gone.' It was a real act of sisterhood, and she was quite a romantic at heart, Betty. She knew that I would be heartbroken for ever, not only about losing Brian, but also missing my final exams and not being a nurse. It all meant the world to me, and she cared that it did. So Betty got me the plane ticket and gave me some money. Then one night I snuck out of the downstairs lounge window, heart in my mouth, holding a little bag, and ran to Clonmel train station. From there I got a train to Dublin and thence onto a plane to England, and escaped. I had already written to Sister Tutor saying I was going to come back somehow, some way, and that I hoped Putney Hospital would take me back again, as promised.

When I got back to Putney I was so happy to find my room still waiting for me. All my friends gave me a heroine's welcome, and they all got in the Merrydown and Woodbines and we sat up late that first night, while I filled them in. Even Percy the porter was pleased to see me. But it had to be straight back to hard work and study, no messing. I had thrown away my tranquillisers, and I was back to being a human being. I had never been so grateful in all my life to empty a bedpan or even a vomit bowl. I told Sister Tutor what had passed, and she was an amazing ally to me: 'You will make an excellent nurse, Mary,' she said, 'but you will have a lot of catching up to do, so you'll have to work hard and concentrate now.' I knew what she meant, so although Brian was waiting for me, and was amazed when I told him all that transpired, he also understood I needed to knuckle down to study for my exams. I wasn't even worried about the Beetle, or Matron, or being carpeted again, so I really put my back into learning and working, and in the summer of 1955 I passed my finals with flying colours. I was so proud that I finally could call myself an SRN, although I would still have another probationary year to complete to get my certificate and badge.

I was finally standing in the queue at my graduation ceremony in June 1955, waiting to receive my SRN badge, certificate and hospital badge from Putney Hospital's Chief Consultant and Matron. I was wearing my black belt, with its special buckle, and my hat with its little string and bow. Of course, when I looked round the room I could see Sister Tutor, and my dear friends, but there was not a single member of my family from Ireland, sadly. However, Brian was there, beaming from the front row and giving me the thumbs up. During my probationary year we were married on 4 December 1956 in Harrow Registry Office. We had no guests at all, just a couple of witnesses. We spent our wedding night seeing Agatha Christie's *Mousetrap* play and staying a night in the Charing Cross Hotel. We had no honeymoon, as we couldn't afford it then, but we were happy. We had waited and I had qualified, and that was what mattered to me. But after the wedding I put my ring on a chain round my neck, and hid it. I didn't want to jeopardise my position as a nurse, and I wanted to complete my probationary year and continue working beyond that, so I hid the fact that

I was married, and we lived very discreetly in a flat in Putney. In a way my mother's crazy plan to kidnap me had backfired on her because, in the end, it had strengthened my resolve even more to succeed in becoming a nurse, live and work in black, Protestant England, and marry a Godforsaken Englishman.

16

Reader, I Married Him … and Carried On Working for the Next Sixty Years …

By 1956 I was a qualified SRN, secretly married (still naughty Mary through and through) and working in all sorts of capacities locally as a nurse while Brian pursued his career. We didn't have much money, but we managed and were happy. I was now living in England and could see my life would remain there for a long time to come. I wanted my family to visit, but they didn't, and my mother still would not forgive me. However, during my early years after training I did all sorts of nursing jobs which I thoroughly enjoyed. I did some midwifery work, but found it was not really for me, and I didn't pursue it further. Then

I worked in a lot of different hospitals, and did a lot of night duties (which Putney had prepared me well for); and I worked regularly in theatre, as a community nurse, and even did a stint in a private hospital, the Nuffield, for a while. Having been trained by the NHS I couldn't get used to having to write down every single thing I had got for a patient, like a toothbrush or a sanitary towel. I wasn't particularly commercially minded, and I felt the private attitude to health actually got in the way of nursing, so I quit that as soon as possible. It wasn't for me.

From being a staff nurse, I soon went on to become a sister myself, and worked nights once my children came along. I had three lovely children who were the apples of my eye: two boys, Christopher and Anthony, and a girl, Jennifer. Brian's work was up and down in sales, so I had to keep on working to bring the money in. I did a lot of night shifts and used my husband's mother, friends, child-minders and a local state nursery to get me through the early years. Nursing was definitely my life, and I was always happy once I was back on the wards, or dealing with some medical problem or other. I loved the camaraderie, and the whole way of life. Sometimes I had to take on some extra part-time work like waitressing to make ends meet. I always gravitated back to nursing full or part time, as the odd jobs were really just to supplement our precarious incomes. I also worked in some elderly care homes, which were horrendous. I remember one place, run by a Harley Street doctor, where the poor elderly inmates were left just one cup of porridge oats to feed them all (seventeen people). That's all there was, a small amount of watery gruel for them to live on. I couldn't bear such meanness, and left there as soon as possible. At another place I worked, which had lots of disabled inmates, we had a riot one night when we took them all up in the centre minibus to Regent Street to see the lights at Christmas, and then got them twenty portions of fish and chips to eat in the bus on the way home. They had a great time, and thoroughly enjoyed themselves, although the bus really stank for ages afterwards.

Sadly, my mother and I could never make peace. I found it very painful that she was never able to be a hands-on grandmother, and didn't send presents to my children for Christmas or birthdays. I think her mind was fixed, and her views were rigid, and she never forgave me for what she thought was my terrible betrayal. Personally, I feel she missed out terribly on her lovely grandchildren's childhoods, and she didn't experience their love and sense of fun, which was a great shame all round. I was sad about it, obviously, and I knew my father would never come over and see me on his own, and sadly he died in 1971. I did see my sisters and brother from time to time, as I visited them and their families, so we managed to remain in good contact until each of them eventually died. Unfortunately, they all died fairly early due to ill health; I believe that the TB had definitely weakened my sisters' hearts and immunity. When my mother got bowel cancer, at the age of sixty, I did visit her, and I offered to nurse her, but she was unforgiving, and so no real reconciliation was possible. She had turned away from me completely. Amazingly, I did found out, however, from the priest, that she had actually been grief-stricken when I'd gone over to England originally, something which she had never really conveyed to me. He had told her to forget that she ever had had a daughter called Mary, and I think that's actually what she did. So, all I had ever had was the anger and the recriminations, and of course the kidnapping. However, I wasn't bitter, as I had chosen my path and followed it, and I was happy in my choices. I did retain my relationship with my siblings and their children throughout, I am pleased to say.

Also, I am sad to say that my marriage to Brian didn't last, despite having three lovely children, and we were divorced in the 1971. I then had to be a lone parent to my three young children, and that proved to be a tough task, but being a resourceful nurse I was always able to get work, and I did a lot of night duties as a sister. I had to exist on very little sleep, and a lot of support from dear friends, but I managed it. I think I always found a way through, and was determined to be there for my children, whatever effort it took. I did marry a second time, but unfortunately it didn't work out.

However, there was a terribly dark time to come for me. Tragedy was to strike, and it would take me years and years to get over it – in fact, I never really did get over it. My wonderful daughter Jennifer was killed at the age of twenty-one by a drunk driver. Her own car had broken down, and she had been out to a pub with friends (she didn't even drink). She had accepted a ten-minute lift home from a stranger, who she didn't know was completely over the limit. It was a freak accident, but the driver hit a lamp-post, and my beautiful Jennifer was decapitated. He ran away with bruises and scratches, with his girlfriend, brother and sister, and abandoned her in his car, but was tracked down through A&E records and prosecuted, thank goodness. However, he only got nine months in jail and I was totally heart-broken. I could not bear the grief of losing my girl, or the ridiculousness of the man's sentence. By now my two sons had left home, and I had worked for years in various hospitals. The stress of losing my daughter was too much, as I loved her dearly, and I had a breakdown. I spent several months, heartbroken, desperately sad and bereft, as my daughter was such a wonderful, lovely girl, and her loss was beyond what I could handle. We were very close and it did feel like the end of the world. I also found out that I had cervical cancer and had a hysterectomy before I was fifty, and gradually pulled through. This was in the early 1980s and all looked very bleak for a while. I think I became quite depressed, feeling I had been through two marriages, lost my beloved daughter, dealt with cancer and had no idea where to go next. For a while I felt totally lost, and I wasn't even interested in going back to work – I felt I had nothing left to give.

Then a dear fellow nurse came to see me one day in 1983, and suggested we go into business together. She could see I was struggling, and I was unusually down and had no direction in life any more. She also knew how much I had loved my daughter, and how bereft I was. When she suggested we set up a business I really thought she was mad, as I didn't have a commercial bone in my body. But she was adamant that we could do it together, and that it would work, and she really thought we should make a go of it. She had noticed a gap in the market for good-quality residential care for the elderly. I had some insurance money after my daughter's death, from an insurance policy she had, and we went to see a business adviser.

Then we sank Jennifer's money, along with some money from my friend, into a property in Palmer's Green, North London, and set up a care home for the elderly, called The Hollies. I'd never done anything like this in my life before, and it was a steep learning curve, but it was a wonderful antidote to all the loss and emptiness I was feeling. We had to take out a mortgage, and it took months to get the business up and running, but it was great to have a project. The house had to pass fire regulations and social service rules, so there was a huge amount for us to get to grips with.

Eventually, we had twelve elderly residents in all, and because we were trained nurses we could attend to their physical needs, look after them when they got sick (so they didn't have to go into hospital), and we also did all sorts of fun things, like their nails, their hair, and so on. I always liked working with the elderly and we had a lot of good times with these people, who were both men and women, some single, some married, some widowed. We really looked after them well, and we had lots of song evenings, games nights and parties. We tried to make it a fun place to be. One particular married couple used to share a room, and the woman had Alzheimer's, and they used to go to bed early together. Then there would be a 'boom' and she'd be on the floor. He'd pick her up, and they'd get into bed together again, then there's be another 'boom' half an hour later, and he'd be on the floor. He insisted on their sleeping together in one tiny single bed, although they had twin beds in their room – I guess they were used to it after a lifetime together. They were a sweet old couple, and we had a ball with those old people: I loved them like my own family. We would have Christmas parties, and little dances, and we did four days on, three days off, and covered the duties, including the nights, all ourselves. Sadly, the regulations of the local authority changed, and made it harder and more expensive for us to run. We were going to lose out unless we bought a bigger property, which meant borrowing more money. Neither of us felt we could do that at our ages, so we were heartbroken as we had to decide to sell the business. (The place is still there, although it's been expanded now.) I loved working with the elderly, but we had to sell up. We both took out about £6,000 each after all was told, and that is how I bought my little one-bedroom flat, to live on my own, after that.

However, I still wanted to work, as I still loved nursing, and I had found working in The Hollies had been very restorative after the loss of my daughter. It actually saved my life. My sons were grown up, and having families of their own now, and I felt I couldn't really face the rest of my life without working. I still loved being involved in all things medical, so I decided to try to find something to do.

Luckily, I saw an advert in a local newspaper for Chase Farm Hospital, in Hertfordshire, who were looking to train up some new phlebotomists (people who take blood samples). I had never done anything like that, but I thought it might be a great thing to do. It was a new skill, and it avoided all the usual heavy lifting and physical work that was involved in nursing. I applied and got the job, and so I was trained as a phlebotomist, and went on to work at Chase Farm for the next fourteen years. I loved the work, as it was light, but interesting, and it was dealing with people all day. I also loved the staff, and I made some very good friends there. I guess I always feel at home with nurses, and we had great laughs, and went out to pubs and parties, and always had a jolly good time at Christmas (including Irish dancing and singing, of course).

I eventually retired from Chase Farm in 1994 and thought that was it, time to hang up my white nurse's coat. However, my local GP's surgery, the Bounds Green Group Practice (BGGP), in Bounds Green, North London, was looking for a phlebotomist to work on the premises. As I was living fairly near by, and had a car, I thought, '*Why not?*' I met with the chief GP, a charming and sincere Dr Schamroth, and soon I was started on my next, and final, career, working in the GP's surgery for four days a week, taking blood. I loved the work, and really enjoyed working with the doctors and practice nurses. I always felt very at home there, and I would get up at six in the morning, winter or summer, come rain or shine, have my breakfast, walk my little Shih Tzu doggies, Bobby and Lottie, and then go in to work.

I worked at the BGGP until November 2013 when I retired reluctantly, at the age of 79. I had worked in the NHS for 62 years by then and think there are few nurses that have worked that long in the service. Every time, before that, when I tried to retire, I would tell Dr Schamroth that I thought it was time I was off, and he would say, 'You can't retire, Mary. Why don't you take Friday off?' So I'd think '*OK*' and carry on. I didn't really do the job for money, as I had my nursing pension, but I did it for the love of the job, and the love of company. Meanwhile, I would spend some of my afternoons and evenings visiting the elderly, and I looked after one particular woman, Connie, until she was ninety-three. She was blind, poor thing, and I'd take her out in the car, or take her to appointments, to go shopping, or help her do things. I actually received an award in 2013 for over 100 hours of volunteering in the community, from the Mayor of Enfield, but I didn't do it for that, of course; I did it because I enjoy the work and I'd rather be out and about doing something than moping round the house, getting bored. On my off days I spend time writing to

David Cameron, telling him to bring back decent standards of hygiene and care in the nursing service: it's essential to keep on top of that, and I should know, as I spent my formative years scrubbing away madly with the carbolic and disinfectant. I still see a few Putney staff for a social occasion from time to time. I still walk my little Jack Russell dog, Jacko, every day in my local park today (sadly, my two other doggies died). I have a gang of friends I meet there, and dish out the odd bit of nursing advice when it's needed. We often end up having a pub lunch together, with the dogs chasing each other in and out of the pond.

I have just turned eighty, but am so thankful for the life that I have had in nursing. I know I've made many mistakes in my life, and I left behind my family in Ireland, and lost two husbands and my beloved daughter, but I have to say I don't have any real regrets. I try to live each day as well as I can, I still like to go out to the pub with my friends, or take my dog to the park, or help to organise the street party, or sit in my back garden, with a glass of chilled white wine, and chat to my neighbours on a sunny afternoon. My cheeky neighbours in the street call me 'Queen Mary' although I have no idea why. I can honestly say I feel I've had the best, most productive and happy of lives working, as a proud Irish nurse, for over sixty-two years in the NHS.